Illinois Homeowners' Guide to Pest Management

Cooperative Extension Service ◆ College of Agricultural, Consumer and Environmental Science
University of Illinois at Urbana-Champaign ◆ Circular 1354

Contents

CHAPTER ONE

Managing Plant Diseases in the Home Landscape

CHAPTER TWO

Controlling Weeds in Home Lawns

CHAPTER THREE

Controlling Weeds in the Home Garden

CHAPTER FOUR

Managing Diseases in the Home Vegetable Garden

CHAPTER FIVE

Managing Insect Pests in the Home, Yard, and Garden

CHAPTER SIX

Managing Pests in Home Fruit Plantings

Appendixes

Managing Plant Diseases in the Home Landscape

2 *Rosa rubra.*
The Red Rose.

4 *Rosa prouincialis minor.*

Diagnosis

The first step in an effective disease management program is proper identification of the problem. That step is often the most difficult as well. It is important to gain a broad knowledge of the various diseases that are likely to occur on a host, as well as the nondisease problems that may have similar symptoms. At the very least, start with a good library of reference books to which you can refer for this information. Keys to help with diagnosis, as well as a list of disease fact sheets, are provided in this chapter.

Disease control measures must start before infection or at the early onset of disease, but preferably before symptoms appear. Disease control programs should ideally begin with the purchase of the best seed or planting materials available and continue throughout the season until the plants or their parts are sold or discarded. In a more realistic scenario, the disease problem is identified one year, nonchemical control measures are instituted the same season, and chemical controls begin at the start of the following season, if necessary.

Plant diseases are either *noninfectious* (also referred to as abiotic) or *infectious* (also referred to as pathogenic). Noninfectious diseases are caused by environmental or cultural conditions, often involving some type of stress. Examples include iron chlorosis, improper watering, or extremes in weather conditions.

Infectious diseases are caused by *pathogens*, living agents that cause disease and may spread from plant to plant. Four types of pathogens cause most infectious diseases of plants: fungi, bacteria, viruses, and nematodes. Plant pathogens, generally microscopic in size, cannot be seen with the unaided eye. The plants they infect, however, develop symptoms that can be seen and that provide clues to the type of pathogen and disease present. Examples of infectious diseases include black spot of rose, dollar spot of turf, and anthracnose of many trees. Examples of symptoms include wilting, leaf spots, and dwarfed growth.

Whether a disease is infectious or noninfectious may be determined by looking at many different species in the same area. Disease pathogens usually infect certain plant species or closely related species, so if different species show similar symp-

Photo by James Schmidt

Fire Blight

toms, or stress, then a noninfectious cause is most likely. Improper conditions, or stress, affect many different species. Also, the noninfectious disease can occur very rapidly as conditions change (for example, when an overnight temperature change causes plants to wilt), whereas infectious disease pathogens generally develop more slowly.

Be alert for multiple causes contributing to plant decline. Often symptoms caused by improper growing conditions, chemical injury, or environmental stress are similar to symptoms caused by infectious disease pathogens. Plants under stress are more susceptible to infectious disease agents, so the disease problem may be secondary to the cause of the stress. Be sure to keep an open mind and gather all the facts before making a diagnosis.

Principles of Disease Control

Management of diseases of plants may involve one or more of the fundamental principles of disease control. These include (1) exclusion, (2) eradication, (3) resistance, and (4) protection. All cultural and chemical practices that are used to keep plants from becoming diseased can be placed into one of these four categories.

Disease-Free Seed

1. **Exclusion** involves preventing the disease-causing organisms and agents from becoming established in or around susceptible plants. Exclusion is achieved through federal or state embargoes; quarantines; inspections; and disinfection of seeds, plants, cuttings, or other propagative plant parts. Other methods include certification of plants and cuttings before shipment, and culture indexing of planting stock to ensure freedom from pathogens. Currently Florida and California have strict laws regulating plant movement into those states. The purpose is to protect the huge plant industry from insects and diseases that are not yet problems.

2. **Eradication** is the elimination of the disease-causing agent or pathogen after it has become established in or on a plant where it is growing or being stored. Eradication involves the removal and destruction of infected plant parts, diseased plants, infected debris, weeds, alternate hosts, and other overwintering host plants. It also involves seed or plant treatment with wet or dry heat or a chemical (such as a multipurpose soil fumigant); crop rotation; and cleaning and disinfecting potting benches, soil bins, greenhouse benches, nursery beds, storage areas, tools, and equipment. Removal of virus-infected plants is a form of eradication.

Infected Leaf

3. **Resistance** involves growing plant species, varieties, or cultivars that are not susceptible to the disease pathogen. Plants have genetic mechanisms for defense against pathogens; and plant breeders work to find plants that are resistant to diseases while maintaining other desirable horticultural qualities. Much less time and effort has been put into developing disease-resistant ornamentals than into field crops, vegetables, and fruits; but resistance is available to many common diseases. Apple scab is an example. This disease is damaging to most of the older crabapple cultivars, but most new cultivars with wonderful flower color can be found with resistance to scab.

4. **Protection** is the placing of a physical or chemical barrier between the susceptible part of the host plant and the disease agent or pathogen. Protection usually means uniform applications of recommended disease control chemicals (including fungicides, bactericides, or nematicides) as dusts, sprays, or soil drenches. Chemicals should be applied to the plant or its propagative parts before the pathogen arrives.

Protective cultural practices include proper spacing of plants; proper time and depth of planting; proper soil reaction (pH); careful handling of plants and propagative parts during harvest, grading, and packing; proper lighting, temperature control, watering, fertilizing, and pruning; and the alteration of the air and soil environment to make it unfavorable for the pathogen to infect, develop, reproduce, or spread during growth, storage, and shipping.

How to Use This Chapter

Disease management involves one or more of the four principles just discussed. In some cases, chemical applications are necessary. This chapter lists registered pesticides for specific plants against specific diseases. Although the non- chemical control measures change little over the years, chemical recommendations may change annually. Product labels also change. **It is your legal responsibility to verify that you are using the product according to its label.** Check the label for changes each time you buy a pesticide. The chapter will be updated when a significant number of chemicals available to the homeowner have label changes. It is not the intent of the authors to promote chemical controls nor to promote one product over another. The intent is to provide a list of registered chemicals, as well as references to other disease control information, so that the homeowner may choose the appropriate methods and proper product for the disease encountered.

Table 1

A series of fact sheets discussing specific diseases of plants is available from the Department of Crop Sciences at the University of Illinois. These fact sheets are the *Report on Plant Disease* series *(RPDs)*. Each fact sheet describes one disease or group of diseases, and discusses host plants, environmental conditions necessary for disease, details on the pathogen, and methods of control. The *RPDs* are an excellent source of information on nonchemical disease control. If resistant plant varieties or cultivars are available, they are usually listed in the *RPD*. Table 1 of this chapter lists the *RPDs* discussing diseases on ornamental plants, turf, and tree fruits. Where specific diseases are listed in other tables, the appropriate *RPD* number is also listed for further reference.

Table 2

This table categorizes turf diseases that a homeowner might encounter, based on the season in which the disease might appear. Nonchemical controls are discussed in the *RPDs* listed in the right-hand column. The chemical options are enumerated in the middle column. To save space (and cost), the chemicals are listed by number codes. Actual chemicals are listed by these same code numbers in Table 7, where both trade names and common names are provided.

Tables 3 and 5

Correct identification of a disease problem is the first step in disease management. Literally hundreds of books are available on the subject of disease identification of ornamental plants. Tables 3 and 5 attempt to present simple keys to disease identification based on symptomology. Table 3 provides a key for diseases of flowers and other nonwoody plants. Use this guide for hosts, including annuals, perennials, and biennials, that do not have woody stems. Table 5 provides a similar key for plants with woody stems, including trees, shrubs, and some vines. These tables are meant to serve as a guide or aid in identification. Use of more detailed reference books often is necessary to make a correct diagnosis.

Report on Plant Disease

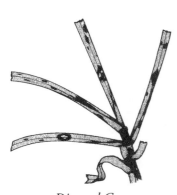

Diseased Grass

Tables 4 and 6

These tables list both nonchemical and chemical controls for use against the common diseases found on flowers and other nonwoody ornamental plants (Table 4), as well as the woody plants (Table 6) found in Illinois. Nonchemical controls are discussed in the *RPD*s listed in the right-hand column. Chemical options are enumerated in the middle column. To save space (and cost), the chemicals are listed by number codes. Actual chemicals are listed by these same code numbers in Table 7, where both trade name and common name are provided. Viral diseases are not listed because chemical controls are not effective against them. In a few cases, a disease is listed even though no chemical is available for control. This was done intentionally to point out that the disease was not inadvertently skipped.

Diseased Leaf

Before using any product, carefully read its label to be certain that it is registered for the host on which you intend to use the product. In this chapter, the authors have grouped some plants. For example, nonbearing apple and pear are listed together. Also, controls for pine, spruce, and fir are listed together. This grouping is done to save space. The diseases and controls are nearly identical on these plants. Always read the product label to identify any host, environmental, or plant-stage interactions that may occur. Only labeled applications are legal.

Some products are available to commercial applicators but not to homeowners. If the product is a restricted-use product (RUP), special licensing is required for buying and applying it. Other unavailable chemicals without the RUP designation may not be produced in homeowner-sized packets due to cost to the producer. Companies such as Ortho and Ferti-lome have filled some of this void of product availability. Still, if products are not available, consult the current *Illinois Commercial Landscape and Turfgrass Pest Management Handbook*. It may be necessary to seek the help of a certified turf or ornamental pesticide applicator.

Table 7

The chemical recommendations that are given as coded numbers in Tables 2, 4, and 6 are listed in Table 7 by code number, trade name, and common name. Should you find a chemical that is registered for use on ornamentals but is not listed, contact the authors.

Additional Help

The University of Illinois Plant Clinic has served as a clearinghouse for plant problems since 1976. Services include plant and insect identification; diagnosis of disease, insect, weed, and chemical injury; nematode assays; and help with nutrient-related problems, as well as recommendations involving these diagnoses. Microscopic examinations, laboratory culturing, virus assays, and nematode assays are a few of the techniques used in the clinic. This multidisciplinary venture involves input from specialists in the areas of botany, entomology, forestry, horticulture, mycology, plant pathology, soils, soil fertility, and weed sciences, as well as others as needed.

Microscope

It is always best to try working through plant problems first with your local Extension educators. These people have a better idea of the local influences of environment, soil type, weather conditions, or other factors that might influence plant health. Many are trained in diagnosis as well. Use the clinic as a laboratory facility to help with more specialized needs or consultations. The Plant Clinic is open from May 1 to September 15. It is located on the South Farms of the Urbana–Champaign campus. The address is

Plant Clinic
1401 W. St. Mary's Rd.
Urbana, IL 61802
(217)333-0519

There is a fee for all samples submitted to the clinic. Checks should be made payable to the University of Illinois. These fees are always subject to change. They are as follow:

General diagnosis (including cultures)	$10
Specialty tests (SCN, PWN, ELISA)*	$15
Other nematodes (usually corn)	$30

*SCN indicates the test for soybean cyst nematode. PWN indicates pinewood nematode analysis. ELISA is a technique used to test for various viral pathogens.

Suggestions for Specimen Collection and Submission

1. Collect fresh samples and send a generous amount of material. It is often helpful to send healthy plant material along with the affected tissue.

2. Ship in a crush-proof container immediately after collecting. If holdover periods are encountered, keep specimens cool. Mail the packages to arrive at the clinic on a weekday.

3. Include a Plant Clinic specimen data form (photocopy from page 129) or equivalent information with each sample.

Note: Diagnosis and recommended controls by the University of Illinois Plant Clinic are based solely on the material and information submitted. The less representative the sample and the less complete the information provided, the greater the chances for misdiagnosis.

Plant Clinic Specimen Data Form

Submitting Plant Specimens for Disease/Injury Diagnosis

Leaf: Collect early and late stages of infection. Press leaves between heavy paper or cardboard. Keep them flat and dry. Do not use plastic.

Fleshy plant parts: Samples with a rot disease should not be sent in advanced stages of decay. Collect fresh specimens with early symptom development.

Canker: Select recently produced cankers. Submit the whole cankered portion if possible; preferably with healthy wood above and below the canker.

Wilt or general decline: Send the entire plant, with roots, if feasible; submit several plants, from healthy to severely infected. Dig, do not pull, the plant from the soil so diseased roots remain intact. If the whole plant cannot be sent, sample areas of active symptom development. Include the intact root system if root rot is suspected. In some cases, photos may be the only way to show the entire sample.

Turf: Submit several 4-inch plugs of grass cut as deeply as the roots hold soil. Plugs should show gradation from healthy to severely diseased. Wrap soil and roots in plastic, but do not cover the blades with plastic.

Submitting Nematode Specimens

Diseases caused by nematodes require special attention. See *Report on Plant Disease*, no. 1100, for detailed instructions on handling and shipping nematode-infested material. Samples for pine wilt should be prepared as detailed in *RPD*, no. 1104. For additional information on how to collect and submit a sample for diagnosis, contact your local Extension office, or call the Plant Clinic.

Table 1. *Report on Plant Disease* **Series**

Report on Plant Disease (*RPD*) publications are available for $1 each from local Illinois Extension offices or the Department of Crop Sciences. Please make check payable to the University of Illinois.

Department of Crop Sciences
Plant Pathology Extension
N-543 Turner Hall
1102 S. Goodwin Ave.
Urbana, IL 61801
(217)333-8375

In the following list, the date in parentheses indicates the most recent update. Numbers in bold print designate *RPD*s printed in color.

Grasses and Turf

400   Recommendations for the Control of Diseases of Turfgrasses (3/89)
401   Slime Molds (4/86)
402   Turfgrass Disease Control (1995)
403   Fairy Rings, Mushrooms, and Puffballs (9/87)
404   Snow Molds of Turfgrasses (5/90)
405   Helminthosporium Leaf Crown and Root Diseases of Lawn Grasses (9/92)
406   Powdery Mildew of Turfgrasses (4/86)
407   Sclerotinia Dollar Spot of Turfgrasses (4/86)
408   Summer Patch and Necrotic Ring Spot of Lawns and Fine Turfgrasses (9/92)
409   Leaf Smuts of Turfgrasses (7/90)
410   Pythium Blight of Turfgrasses (10/92)
411   Rhizoctonia Diseases of Turfgrasses (5/86)
412   Rusts of Turfgrasses (6/87)
413   Red Thread and Pink Patch of Turfgrasses (5/89)
414   Bacterial Wilt and Decline of Turfgrasses (10/87)
415   Yellow Tuft on Downy Mildew of Turfgrasses (4/88)
416   Anthracnose of Turfgrasses (8/88)
417   Minor Leaf Spot and Blight Diseases of Turfgrasses (10/88)

Ornamentals

600   Fungal Leaf Spots of Black Walnut (6/87)
601   Leaf Diseases of Mountain-Laurel (6/82)
602   Armillaria Root Rot of Trees and Shrubs (12/88)
603   Iron Chlorosis of Woody Plants: Cause and Control (1996)
604   Cytospora Canker of Spruce (1996)
605   Leaf Rusts of Poplars and Willows in the Midwest (2/90)
606   Phomopsis Canker and Dieback of Russian Olive (6/87)
607   Bacterial Disease of Geraniums (4/90)
608   Virus Diseases of Geranium (9/89)
609   Tulip Fire or Botrytis Blight (7/82)
610   Black Spot of Rose (10/87)
611   Powdery Mildew of Roses (3/88)
612   Gladiolus Viruses (8/83)
613   Leaf Spots, Anthracnose, and Scab of Pansy and Violet (9/83)
614   Common Viruses of Orchids (5/90)
615   Damping-off and Root Rots of House Plants and Garden Flowers (2/88)
616   Bacterial Diseases of Anthurium, Dieffenbachia, Philodendron, and Syngonium (5/90)
617   Powdery Mildews of Ornamentals (7/87)

618   Oak Wilt and Its Control (1996)
619   Fasciation, or Leafy Gall (4/91)
620   Leaf Scorch of Woody Plants (12/88)
621   Anthracnose Diseases of Shade Trees (7/90)
622   Phomopsis Twig Blight of Juniper (2/88)
623   Botrytis Blight or Gray Mold of Ornamental Plants (1/90)
624   Needle Blights and Needle Casts of Pines (11/87)
625   Sphaeropsis Blight or Diplodia Tipblight of Pines (5/88)
626   Rose Cane Cankers (5/90)
627   Hollyhock Rust (2/82)
628   Iris Leaf Spot (4/82)
629   Oedema or Corky Scab (4/82)
630   Rose Rusts (4/89)
631   Red Spot, Leaf Blotch of Peonies (4/82)
632   Rose Viruses (9/88)
633   Crown, Rhizome, and Bulb Rots of Iris (9/82)
634   Tulip Breaking or Mosaic (9/90)
635   Snapdragon Rust (7/82)
636   Canker and Dieback Disease of Woody Plants (1995)
637   Leaf Spot or Blight of Hawthorn (7/87)
638   Firethorn (Pyracantha) Scab (1/83)
639   Azalea Leaf and Flower Gall (10/82)
640   Stem Blight of Vinca Minor (1/83)
641   Decline and Dieback of Trees and Shrubs (1995)
642   Wood Rots and Decay (11/90)
643   Trees Resistant or Susceptible to Disease (9/87)
647   Dutch Elm Diseases and Its Control (1995)
648   Leaf Spot Diseases of Shade and Ornamental Trees in the Midwest (5/88)
649   Pachysandra Leaf and Stem Blight (9/83)
650   Fusarium Wilt Diseases of Herbaceous Ornamentals (2/88)
651   Gladiolus Corm Rots (11/83)
652   Leaf Spot Diseases of English Ivy (11/83)
653   Pepperomia Disease (4/88)
654   Mosaic Diseases of Iris (4/88)
655   Common Leaf Diseases of Zinnia (10/87)
656   Bacterial Wetwood and Slime Flux of Landscape Trees (4/89)
657   Downy Mildew of Snapdragons (12/88)
658   Geranium Rust (1/89)
659   Bacterial Leaf Spot of Begonia (2/89)
660   Elm Yellows on Phloem Necrosis and Its Control (5/90)
661   Cytospora Canker of Poplar and Willows (5/90)
662   Witches' Broom of Hackberry (7/89)
663   Oak Leaf Blister (9/90)
664   Phytophthora Root Rot or Wilt of Rhododendrons and Azaleas in the Midwest (1990)
665   Tomato Spotted Wilt Virus (4/91)
666   Rose Rosette Disease (10/91)

Tree Fruits

800   Cherry Leaf Spot (1995)
801   Fire Blight (10/87)
802   Cedar–Apple and Related Rusts (6/87)
803   Apple and Crabapple Scab (1994)
804   Brown Rot of Stone Fruits (5/88)
805   Peach Leaf Curl and Plum Pockets (5/88)

Miscellaneous

Table 2. Products Labeled for Turfgrass Diseases

Turfgrass diseases and when they typically appear	Labeled pesticides[a]	Additional information
Cold weather (<32–45°F); usually winter		
Snow molds (pink snow mold, gray snow mold)	11 (pink snow mold only), 18, 20 (gray snow mold only).	See *RPD* 404.
Cool weather (45–60°F); usually early spring or late fall		
Powdery mildew	18.	See *RPD* 406.
Rust	8, 12, 15, 16, 18, 20.	See *RPD* 412.
Smut	11, 18.	See *RPD* 409.
Warm to hot weather (60–75°F or greater); usually late spring, summer, or early fall		
Dollar spot	8, 11, 12, 15, 16, 18, 20.	See *RPD* 407.
Fairy rings	15.	See *RPD* 403.
"Helminthosporium" diseases (*Bipolaris, Drechslera* spp.)	8, 11, 12, 14, 15, 16, 20.	See *RPD* 405.
Necrotic ring spot and summer patch (Fusarium patch or frog eye)	18.	See *RPD* 408.
Pythium blight	15.	See *RPD* 410.
Slime molds	Controlled by any fungicide listed under "Helminthosporium" diseases.	See *RPD* 401.
Rhizoctona brown patch	8, 11, 12, 14, 15, 16, 18, 20.	See *RPD* 411.

[a]Refer to Table 7 for actual pesticide product names. Before using any product, carefully read its label to identify any varietal, environmental, or plant-stage interactions that may occur. Repeated, exclusive use of a product may lead to pesticide resistance and the loss of pest control. Whenever possible, alternate or mix products to reduce the development of pest resistance, as directed by the labels. See the *Illinois Commercial Landscape and Turfgrass Pest Management Handbook* (updated annually) for additional pesticide products available to commercial applicators.

Table 3. Disease Symptoms of Flowers and Nonwoody Ornamentals

General symptoms	Specific symptoms	Disease
Leaves Leaves show small to large, definite spots that vary in size, shape, and color.	Small dark specks are present, indicating fungal fruiting bodies; spots often roundish, with dark margins.	Fungal leaf spot Scab Spot anthracnose
	Dark, water-soaked angular spots in leaves; spots later turn gray, brown, reddish brown, or black; margin usually water-soaked.	Bacterial leaf spot or blight
	Irregular, often large, dead areas in leaves.	Leaf blight or blotch Anthracnose
Leaves spotted or blighted; later covered with dusty mold growth.	Tan to gray, coarse mold.	Botrytis blight or gray mold
	White to light gray mold:	
	Powdery to mealy; easily wiped off.	Powdery mildew
	Powdery white, raised pustules on underleaf surface; may later turn yellow, then brown.	White rust
	Light gray to pale purplish downy growth on underleaf surface.	Downy mildew
	Black mold:	
	Sooty or crusty; easily wiped off.	Sooty mold or blotch
	Sooty mold inside "blisters," or galls.	Smut
	Yellow, orange, reddish orange, reddish brown, chocolate brown, or black mold in raised pustules.	Rust
Leaves with yellow to brown or black angular spots or stripes; plants stunted or bushy.		Foliar nematodes
Leaves mottled light and dark green or yellow; often stunted, curled, and crinkled.	May form an irregular light and dark green mosaic or mottled pattern.	Viruses, including mosaic; mottle; crinkle; streak; ringspot or spotted wilt.
Leaves and shoots stunted or dwarfed and erect; appear "bunchy"; younger parts uniformly yellow, sometimes red or purple.	Yellow-green or reddish brown rings, "oakleaf," "watermark," or line patterns in leaves. Discoloration inside lower stem.	Yellows Dwarf Stunt Wilt disease

Table 3. Disease Symptoms of Flowers and Nonwoody Ornamentals (cont.)

General symptoms	Specific symptoms	Disease
Leaves wilt, wither, and die; may involve part or all of the plant.	Leaves wilt, wither, and die from stem or crown rot, root rot, drought or excess water, transplant shock, injury from insects or other animals, fertilizer or pesticide injury, an excess of soluble salts, frost, other mechanical injuries.	Miscellaneous diseases and injuries
Stems and Branches Plants lack vigor; leaves are small and pale, may later wilt or turn yellow.	Seedlings collapse and die; stand is poor.	Damping-off Seed rot
	Stems of older plants are water-soaked or discolored and decayed, often just at the base.	Stem or crown rot
	Stems or branches show definitely marked, discolored (often sunken) dead areas; parts beyond may wither and die.	Canker or dieback
	Shoots are often dwarfed or aborted; leaves are distorted; cauliflowerlike growth may appear at the soil line.	Leaf gall or fasciation
	Rough, swollen gall (either flesh-colored, greenish, or dark) usually found at or near the soil line.	Crown gall
Flowers Flowers are spotted, often wither or rot; may be covered with mold growth.		Flower or blosson blight
Flowers are blotched or streaked with white or yellow.		Mosaic or flower breaking
Flowers are greenish yellow, dwarfed, aborted, or absent.		Aster yellows
Roots, Bulbs, Corms, and Tubers Plants lose vigor, often are stunted; may turn pale or yellow; tops may wilt and die back.	Roots decay; feeder roots die back; may be covered with mold.	Root rot
	Bulb, corm, or tuber decays; may be covered mold.	Bulb, corm, or tuber rot
	Rough, roundish galls form on roots, corms, or tubers.	Crown gall
Roots damaged.	Lack of hairy roots; root browning or galling.	Nematodes

Table 4. Products Labeled for Specific Flowers and Other Nonwoody Ornamentals

Plant and disease	Labeled pesticides[a]	Additional information
African violet *(Saintpaulia)*		
Botrytis blight	2, 4, 9, 11, 15, 21.	See *RPD* 623.
Powdery mildew	6, 9, 11, 15, 19, 21.	See *RPD* 617.
Fungal crown and stem rots	9, 11, 15.	See *RPD* 615.
Ageratum		
Cercospora leaf spot Powdery mildew	4, 6, 9, 11, 18, 19, 24.	See *RPD* 617.
Rust	4, 6, 18, 24.	No *RPD.*
Damping-off Fungal crown and root rots	9, 11.	See *RPD* 615.
Botrytis blight	9, 11.	See *RPD* 623.
Ajuga		
Sclerotium (crown) rot	11.	See *RPD* 615.
Powery mildew	6, 9, 11, 19.	See *RPD* 617.
Fungal leaf spots Botrytis blight	9, 11.	See *RPD* 623.
Fungal root rots *(Pythium, Phytophthora)*	None available to homeowner.	See *RPD* 615.
Alyssum		
Fungal root and crown rots	9, 11.	See *RPD* 615.
Botrytis blight	9, 11.	See *RPD* 623.
Artemisia		
Botrytis blight	2, 9, 11.	See *RPD* 623.
Fungal root rots	9, 11.	See *RPD* 615.
Aster, China *(Callistephus)*		
Botrytis blight (bud and stem rot and petal blight)	4, 9, 11.	See *RPD* 623.
Powdery mildew	6, 9, 11, 15, 19, 24.	See *RPD* 617.
Rust	3, 4, 6, 11, 18, 22, 23, 24.	No *RPD.*

[a]Refer to Table 7 for actual pesticide product names. Before using any product, carefully read its label to identify any varietal, environmental, or plant-stage interactions that may occur. Repeated, exclusive use of a product may lead to pesticide resistance and the loss of pest control. Whenever possible, alternate or mix products to reduce the development of pest resistance, as directed by the labels. See the *Illinois Commercial Landscape and Turfgrass Pest Management Handbook* (updated annually) for additional pesticide products available to commercial applicators.

Table 4. Products Labeled for Specific Flowers and Other Nonwoody Ornamentals (cont.)

Plant and disease	Labeled pesticides[a]	Additional information
Aster, China *(Callistephus)* **(cont.)** Fungal leaf spots		
Rhizoctonia stem (crown) and root rot	9, 11.	See *RPD* 615.
Sclerotinia or cottony stem rot	9, 11.	No *RPD*.
Other fungal rot rots	9.	See *RPD* 615, 650.
Aster yellows	Apply insecticides at recommended frequencies.	Six-spotted leafhoppers are vectors of the aster yellows phytoplasma.
Baby's breath—See *Gypsophila.*		
Balsam Botrytis blight	9, 11.	See *RPD* 623.
Fungal root and crown rots	9, 11.	See *RPD* 615.
Begonia Botrytis blight, leaf spot, and stem rot Other fungal leaf spots	2, 3, 4, 9, 11, 15, 21.	See *RPD* 623.
Powdery mildew	6, 9, 11, 15, 18, 19, 21, 22.	See *RPD* 617.
Fungal root, stem, or crown rots	9, 11, 15.	See *RPD* 615.
Damping-off Tuber rot	14.	See *RPD* 615.
Bacterial leaf spot	3, 4, 21.	See *RPD* 659.
Bleeding heart *(Dicentra)* Botrytis blight	9, 11.	See *RPD* 623.
Calendula Fungal leaf spots	6, 11.	No *RPD*.
Powdery mildew	6, 9, 11, 15, 19, 22, 23, 24.	See *RPD* 617.
Rust	24.	No *RPD*.
Rhizoctonia or Schlerotinia (cottony) stem and root rot	9, 11.	See *RPD* 615.
Pythium and Phytophthora root rot	None available to homeowner.	See *RPD* 615.

[a]Refer to Table 7 for actual pesticide product names. Before using any product, carefully read its label to identify any varietal, environmental, or plant-stage interactions that may occur. Repeated, exclusive use of a product may lead to pesticide resistance and the loss of pest control. Whenever possible, alternate or mix products to reduce the development of pest resistance, as directed by the labels. See the *Illinois Commercial Landscape and Turfgrass Pest Management Handbook* (updated annually) for additional pesticide products available to commercial applicators.

Table 4. Products Labeled for Specific Flowers and Other Nonwoody Ornamentals (cont.)

Plant and disease	Labeled pesticides[a]	Additional information
Canna		
Rust	6, 18,	No *RPD*.
Fungal leaf spots	3, 11.	No *RPD*.
Carnation, Pinks *(Dianthus)*		
Anthracnose Alternaria branch rot and leaf spot Greasy blotch Other fungal leaf spots	1, 2, 3, 4, 5, 11, 14, 17, 20.	No *RPD*.
Rust	1, 4, 6, 14, 18, 22, 23, 24.	No *RPD*.
Botrytis blight	2, 3, 4, 5, 9, 11, 15, 17, 20, 21.	See *RPD* 623.
Rhizoctonia stem rot	9, 11, 15.	No *RPD*.
Fusarium root rot	9, 11, 15.	See *RPD* 615, 650,
Powdery mildew	6, 9, 11, 18, 19, 24.	See *RPD* 617.
Phthium root rot Phytophthora root rot Damping-off	1.	See *RPD* 615.
Celosia		
Fungal root and crown rots	9, 11.	See *RPD* 615.
Botrytis blight	9, 11.	See *RPD* 623.
Other fungal leaf spots and blights	4, 11.	No *RPD*.
***Chrysanthemum* (Shasta and Painted daisy, not Transvaal daisy)**		
Aschchyta stem and ray blight Septoria and other fungal leaf spots Anthracnose	1, 2, 3, 4, 5, 6, 8, 11, 12, 13, 20.	No *RPD*.
Rust	2, 4, 6, 18, 24.	No *RPD*.
Botrytis blight	1, 2, 3, 4, 5, 8, 9, 11, 12, 14, 15, 16, 21.	See *PRD* 623.
Powdery mildew	6, 9, 11, 15, 18, 19, 21, 24.	No *RPD*.
Nematodes	None available to homeowner.	See *RPD* 1103.

[a]Refer to Table 7 for actual pesticide product names. Before using any product, carefully read its label to identify any varietal, environmental, or plant-stage interactions that may occur. Repeated, exclusive use of a product may lead to pesticide resistance and the loss of pest control. Whenever possible, alternate or mix products to reduce the development of pest resistance, as directed by the labels. See the *Illinois Commercial Landscape and Turfgrass Pest Management Handbook* (updated annually) for additional pesticide products available to commercial applicators.

Table 4. Products Labeled for Specific Flowers and Other Nonwoody Ornamentals (cont.)

Plant and disease	Labeled pesticides[a]	Additional information
***Chrysanthemum* (Shasta and Painted daisy, not Transvaal daisy) (cont.)**		
Fungal root, stem, or root rots	1, 9, 11.	See *RPD* 615, 650.
Aster yellows Spotted wilt	Apply insecticides at recommended intervals.	Six-spotted leafhoppers are vectors of aster yellows' mycoplasma. Thrips transmit the spotted wilt virus.
Bacterial wilt	10, 21.	Follow label directions.
Clematis		
Ascochyta leaf spot and stem rot	6, 11.	No *RPD*.
Coleus *(Plectranthus)*		
Powdery mildew Rust	9, 11, 24.	No *RPD*.
Botrytis blight	4, 9, 11, 21.	See *RPD* 623.
Root and crown rots	9, 11.	See *RPD* 615.
Daffodil—See *Narcissus.*		
Dahlia		
Botrytis flower blight or gray mold Fungal leaf spots and blights	3, 4, 5, 9, 11, 13, 15.	See *RPD* 623.
Powdery mildew	6, 9, 11, 15, 18, 19, 22, 23, 24.	See *RPD* 617.
Fungal crown and root rot	9, 11.	See *RPD* 615, 650.
Daisies—See *Chrysanthemum* or *Gerbera.*		
Daphne		
Phytophthora and Phythium root rots	None available to homeowner.	See *RPD* 615, 650.
***Delphinium* (Larkspur)**		
Sclerotium root and crown rot Schlerotinia wilt	9, 11.	See *RPD* 615.
Other fungal root and crown rots	9, 11.	See *RPD* 650.
Rust	4, 6.	No *RPD*.

[a]Refer to Table 7 for actual pesticide product names. Before using any product, carefully read its label to identify any varietal, environmental, or plant-stage interactions that may occur. Repeated, exclusive use of a product may lead to pesticide resistance and the loss of pest control. Whenever possible, alternate or mix products to reduce the development of pest resistance, as directed by the labels. See the *Illinois Commercial Landscape and Turfgrass Pest Management Handbook* (updated annually) for additional pesticide products available to commercial applicators.

Table 4. Products Labeled for Specific Flowers and Other Nonwoody Ornamentals (cont.)

Plant and disease	Labeled pesticides[a]	Additional information
***Delphinium* (Larkspur) (cont.)**		
Powdery mildew	6, 9, 11, 18, 19, 22.	See *RPD* 617.
Fungal leaf spots	3, 4, 11.	No *RPD*.
Botrytis blight	4, 9, 11, 21.	See *RPD* 623.
***Dianthus*—See Carnation.**		
Dusty miller *(Centaurea)*		
Fungal leaf spots	3, 4, 11.	No *RPD*.
Fungal root and crown rots	9, 11.	See *RPD* 615.
Fuchsia		
Botrytis blight	4, 9, 11, 15, 21.	See *RPD* 623.
Rust	4, 6, 15, 24.	No *RPD*.
Gazania		
Botrytis blight	9.	See *RPD* 623.
Geranium *(Pelargonium)*		
Botrytis blight	2, 3, 4, 5, 8, 9, 12, 13, 15, 16, 17, 20, 21.	See *RPD* 623.
Bacterial leaf spots	21.	No *RPD*.
Fungal leaf spots	3, 4, 13.	No *RPD*.
Powdery mildew	9, 18, 19.	See *RPD* 617.
Downy mildew	3, 4, 15.	No *RPD*.
Rust	2, 4, 6, 15, 18, 20.	See *RPD* 658.
Rhizoctonia root and stem rot	9.	See *RPD* 615.
Blackleg *(Phythium)*	None available to homeowner.	See *RPD* 615.
Other fungal root rots Damping-off	9.	See *RPD* 615, 650.
***Gerbera* (Transvaal daisy)**		
Phytophthora root rot	None available to homeowner.	See *RPD* 615.
Powdery mildew	6, 9, 19, 21.	See *RPD* 617.

[a]Refer to Table 7 for actual pesticide product names. Before using any product, carefully read its label to identify any varietal, environmental, or plant-stage interactions that may occur. Repeated, exclusive use of a product may lead to pesticide resistance and the loss of pest control. Whenever possible, alternate or mix products to reduce the development of pest resistance, as directed by the labels. See the *Illinois Commercial Landscape and Turfgrass Pest Management Handbook* (updated annually) for additional pesticide products available to commercial applicators.

Table 4. Products Labeled for Specific Flowers and Other Nonwoody Ornamentals (cont.)

Plant and disease	Labeled pesticides[a]	Additional information
***Gerbera* (Transvaal daisy) (cont.)**		
Botrytis blight	4, 9, 21.	See *RPD* 623.
Schlerotinia blight	None available to homeowner.	Follow label directions.
Gladiolus		
Fungal corm rots (Fusarium yellows, Penicillium, Stromatinia, and others)	1, 3, 9, 14, 15.	See *RPD* 615, 650, 651.
Bacterial leaf spots	4.	No *RPD*.
Botrytis leaf and flower spot and corm rot	1, 2, 3, 4, 5, 9, 11, 13, 15, 20.	See *RPD* 623.
Powdery mildew	6, 9, 11, 19.	See *RPD* 617.
Fungal leaf spots	2, 3, 4, 5, 11, 20.	No *RPD*.
Nematodes	None available to homeowner.	See *RPD* 1103.
Gloxinia *(Sinningia)*		
Botrytis bud and flower rot	9, 11, 21.	See *RPD* 623.
Fungal crown rot Leaf and tuber rot	9, 11.	See *RPD* 615.
***Gynura* (Velvet plant)**		
Fungal root and crown rots	9, 11.	See *RPD* 615.
Botrytis blight	9, 11.	See *RPD* 623.
***Gypsophila* (Baby's breath)**		
Botrytis blight	4, 9, 11.	See *RPD* 623.
Phytophthora crown and root rot Phythium root rot	None available to homeowner.	See *RPD* 615.
Hollyhock *(Alcea)*		
Rust Fungal leaf spots Anthracnose	2, 4, 6, 11, 13, 15, 20.	See *RPD* 627.
Powdery mildew	6, 11, 19.	See *RPD* 617.
Hosta		
Bacterial leaf spot	3.	No *RPD*.

[a]Refer to Table 7 for actual pesticide product names. Before using any product, carefully read its label to identify any varietal, environmental, or plant-stage interactions that may occur. Repeated, exclusive use of a product may lead to pesticide resistance and the loss of pest control. Whenever possible, alternate or mix products to reduce the development of pest resistance, as directed by the labels. See the *Illinois Commercial Landscape and Turfgrass Pest Management Handbook* (updated annually) for additional pesticide products available to commercial applicators.

Table 4. Products Labeled for Specific Flowers and Other Nonwoody Ornamentals (cont.)

Plant and disease	Labeled pesticides[a]	Additional information
Hosta (cont.)		
Fungal crown and root rots	9, 11.	See *RPD* 615.
Hyacinth *(Hyacinthus)*		
Botrytis blight	9, 11.	See *RPD* 623.
Fungal bulb rots	11, 15.	See *RPD* 615.
Hydrangea—See Table 6.		
Impatiens		
Fungal root and crown rots	9, 11.	See *PRD* 615.
Botrytis blight	4, 9, 11, 21.	See *RPD* 623.
Powdery mildew	9, 11, 21.	See *RPD* 617.
Bacterial leaf spot	3, 21.	No *RPD*.
Iris		
Fungal leaf spots Rust Botrytis blossom blight	2, 3, 4, 6, 8, 9, 11, 12, 13, 16, 20, 21.	See *RPD* 623, 628.
Fungal crown, rhizome, and bulb rots	9, 11, 15.	See *RPD* 615, 633, 650.
Bacterial soft rot and rhizome rot	Apply insecticides at recommended intervals.	The soft rot bacteria enter through fresh iris borer wounds and other injuries.
Nematodes	None available to homeowner.	See *RPD* 1103.
Ivy, English *(Hedera helix)*		
Fungal spots and blights of leaf, stem, and twig	4, 6, 11, 13.	See *RPD* 652.
Fungal root and crown rot	9, 11.	See *RPD* 615.
Botrytis blight	9, 11, 21.	See *RPD* 623.
Bacterial leaf spot	3, 21.	No *RPD*.
Larkspur—See *Delphinium*.		
Liatris		
Botrytis blight	9, 11.	See *RPD* 623.

[a]Refer to Table 7 for actual pesticide product names. Before using any product, carefully read its label to identify any varietal, environmental, or plant-stage interactions that may occur. Repeated, exclusive use of a product may lead to pesticide resistance and the loss of pest control. Whenever possible, alternate or mix products to reduce the development of pest resistance, as directed by the labels. See the *Illinois Commercial Landscape and Turfgrass Pest Management Handbook* (updated annually) for additional pesticide products available to commercial applicators.

Table 4. Products Labeled for Specific Flowers and Other Nonwoody Ornamentals (cont.)

Plant and disease	Labeled pesticides[a]	Additional information
Lily *(Lilium)* Fungal root and bulb rots	3, 9, 11, 15.	See *RPD* 615.
Botrytis flower blight and leaf spot or blight	2, 3, 4, 5, 9, 11, 13, 17, 20, 21.	See *RPD* 623.
Viral diseases	Apply recommended insecticides to prevent insect vectors from feeding.	No *RPD.*
Lobelia **(Cardinal flower)** Fungal root and crown rots	9, 11.	See *RPD* 615.
Botrytis blight	9, 11.	See *RPD* 623.
Other fungal leaf spots and blights	4, 11.	No *RPD.*
Lupine *(Lupinus)* Botrytis blight	9, 11.	See *RPD* 623.
Marigold *(Tagetes)* Botrytis blight	2, 3, 4, 9, 11, 21.	See *RPD* 623.
Rust	6, 18, 24.	No *RPD.*
Fungal leaf spots	3, 4, 11, 18.	No *RPD.*
Phytophthora stem rot and wilt	None available to homeowner.	See *RPD* 615.
Rhizoctonia root rot	9, 11.	See *RPD* 615.
Monarda **(Bee balm)** Botrytis blight	9, 11.	See *RPD* 623.
Narcissus **(Daffodil)** Fungal bulb rots	9, 11, 15.	See *RPD* 615, 650.
Botrytis blight Fungal leaf spots and leaf scorch	2, 3, 4, 9, 11.	See *RPD* 623.
Nasturtium *(Tropaeolum)* Botrytis blight	9, 11.	See *RPD* 623.
Fungal leaf spots	3, 4, 11.	No *RPD.*
Fungal root and crown rots	9, 11.	See *RPD* 615.

[a]Refer to Table 7 for actual pesticide product names. Before using any product, carefully read its label to identify any varietal, environmental, or plant-stage interactions that may occur. Repeated, exclusive use of a product may lead to pesticide resistance and the loss of pest control. Whenever possible, alternate or mix products to reduce the development of pest resistance, as directed by the labels. See the *Illinois Commercial Landscape and Turfgrass Pest Management Handbook* (updated annually) for additional pesticide products available to commercial applicators.

Table 4. Products Labeled for Specific Flowers and Other Nonwoody Ornamentals (cont.)

Plant and disease	Labeled pesticides[a]	Additional information
Orchid		
Black rot	9, 11, 15.	See *RPD* 615.
Damping-off and root rot		
Botrytis flower spot or blight or gray mold	4, 9, 11, 21.	See *RPD* 623.
Rust	4, 6, 24.	No *RPD*.
Pachysandra		
Volutella leaf and stem blight or canker	2, 3, 4, 20.	See *RPD* 649.
Botrytis blight	2, 4, 9, 11.	See *RPD* 623.
Pansy, violet (*Viola,* not African violet)		
Anthracnose	2, 3, 4, 5, 9, 11, 17, 21.	See *RPD* 613, 623.
Scab		
Fungal leaf spot		
Botrytis blight or gray mold		
Rust	4, 6, 9, 11, 18, 19.	See *RPD* 617.
Powdery mildew		
Downy mildew	3, 4, 13.	No *RPD*.
Seed rot	None available to homeowner.	See *RPD* 615, 650.
Damping-off and seedling blights		
Pelargonium—See Geranium.		
Peony (*Paeonia*)		
Botrytis blight	3, 4, 5, 9, 11, 13, 15.	See *RPD* 623, 631.
Red spot, leaf blotch, and measles		
Phytophthora blight	4, 5.	See *RPD* 615.
Nematodes	None available to homeowner.	See *RPD* 1103.
Periwinkle (*Vinca minor*)		
Botrytis blight	11, 21.	See *RPD* 623.
Other fungal leaf spots and blights	11.	No *RPD*.
Phoma stem blight	3, 4.	No *RPD*.
Fungal root and crown rots	9, 11.	See *RPD* 615.

[a]Refer to Table 7 for actual pesticide product names. Before using any product, carefully read its label to identify any varietal, environmental, or plant-stage interactions that may occur. Repeated, exclusive use of a product may lead to pesticide resistance and the loss of pest control. Whenever possible, alternate or mix products to reduce the development of pest resistance, as directed by the labels. See the *Illinois Commercial Landscape and Turfgrass Pest Management Handbook* (updated annually) for additional pesticide products available to commercial applicators.

Table 4. Products Labeled for Specific Flowers and Other Nonwoody Ornamentals (cont.)

Plant and disease	Labeled pesticides[a]	Additional information
Petunia		
Botrytis blight, leaf blotch, and flower bight	2, 4, 6, 9, 11, 20, 21.	See *RPD* 623.
Fungal leaf spots	6.	No *RPD*.
Powdery mildew Rust	4, 6, 9, 11, 18, 19, 24.	See *RPD* 617.
Fungal root and crown or root rots (*Pythium* and *Rhizoctonia*)	9, 11.	See *RPD* 615.
Philodendron		
Bacterial leaf spot	3, 10.	No *RPD*.
Fungal leaf spots Botrytis blight Phythophthora blight	2, 4, 8, 9, 11, 20.	See *RPD* 623.
Damping-off Root and stem rots	7, 9, 15.	See *RPD* 615.
Nematodes	None available to homeowner.	See *RPD* 1103.
Phlox		
Powdery mildew	6, 9 11, 19, 22, 23.	See *RPD* 617.
Fungal leaf spots Rust Botrytis blight Flower blight	2, 3, 4, 6, 9, 11, 13, 21.	See *RPD* 623.
Fungal root rots	9, 11.	See *RPD* 615.
Pinks—See Carnation.		
Primrose *(Primula)*		
Botrytis blight	9, 11, 21.	See *RPD* 623.
Fungal leaf spots	11.	No *RPD*.
Rust	6.	No *RPD*.
Fungal root and crown rot	9, 11.	See *RPD* 615.
Rose *(Rosa)*—See Table 6.		

[a]Refer to Table 7 for actual pesticide product names. Before using any product, carefully read its label to identify any varietal, environmental, or plant-stage interactions that may occur. Repeated, exclusive use of a product may lead to pesticide resistance and the loss of pest control. Whenever possible, alternate or mix products to reduce the development of pest resistance, as directed by the labels. See the *Illinois Commercial Landscape and Turfgrass Pest Management Handbook* (updated annually) for additional pesticide products available to commercial applicators.

Table 4. Products Labeled for Specific Flowers and Other Nonwoody Ornamentals (cont.)

Plant and disease	Labeled pesticides[a]	Additional information
Saintpaulia—See African violet.		
***Salvia* (Sage)**		
Botrytis blight	4, 9, 11.	See *RPD* 623.
Fungal leaf spots	6, 11.	No *RPD*.
Powdery mildew	9, 11, 18, 19, 24.	See *RPD* 617.
Rust	4, 18, 24.	No *RPD*.
Fungal root and crown rots	9, 11.	See *RPD* 615.
Scilla		
Botrytis bulb rot Sclerotinia blub rot	9.	See *RPD* 615.
Shasta daisy—See *Chrysanthemum.*		
Snapdragon *(Antirrhinum)* Anthracnose Phyllosticta leaf and stem blight Other fungal leaf spots	3, 4, 11, 15.	No *RPD*.
Botrytis blight	2, 3, 4, 9, 11, 21.	See *RPD* 623.
Rust Downy mildew	3, 4, 5, 6, 15, 18, 24.	See *RPD* 635, 657.
Powdery mildew	6, 9, 11, 15, 18, 19, 22, 23, 24.	See *RPD* 617.
Damping-off Rhizoctonia stem and root rot or wirestem	9, 11.	See *RPD* 615.
Pythium and Phytophthora crown and root rots	None available to homeowner.	See *RPD* 615.
Sclerotinia root and crown rot	None available to homeowner.	See *RPD* 615.
Nematodes	None available to homeowner.	See *RPD* 1103.
Statice *(Limonium)* Anthracnose Cersospora, Alternaria, and Botrytis leaf blights	2, 4, 9, 11, 20.	See *RPD* 623.
Phythium crown and root rots	None available to homeowner.	See *RPD* 615.

[a]Refer to Table 7 for actual pesticide product names. Before using any product, carefully read its label to identify any varietal, environmental, or plant-stage interactions that may occur. Repeated, exclusive use of a product may lead to pesticide resistance and the loss of pest control. Whenever possible, alternate or mix products to reduce the development of pest resistance, as directed by the labels. See the *Illinois Commercial Landscape and Turfgrass Pest Management Homent Handbook* (updated annually) for additional pesticide products available to commercial applicators.

Table 4. Products Labeled for Specific Flowers and Other Nonwoody Ornamentals (cont.)

Plant and disease	Labeled pesticides[a]	Additional information
Sweetpea *(Lathyrus)* Powdery mildew	3, 6, 9, 11, 18, 19.	See *RPD* 617.
Botrytis blight	9, 11, 21.	See *RPD* 623.
Fungal leaf spots	11.	No *RPD*.
Fungal root and stem rots	9, 11.	See *RPD* 615.
Transvaal daisy—See *Gerbera.*		
Tulip *(Calochortus)* Fire or Botrytis bight	2, 4, 9, 11, 13.	See *RPD* 609, 623.
Fungal bulb rots	3, 9, 11, 15.	See *RPD* 615, 650.
Verbena Fungal leaf spots	4, 11.	No *RPD*.
Bacterial leaf spot	3.	No *RPD*.
Botrytis blight	11.	See *RPD* 623.
Powdery mildew	6, 9, 11, 19.	See *RPD* 617.
Rhizoctonia stem and root rot	9, 11.	See *RPD* 615.
Fungal root and crown rot *(Pythium, Phythophthora)*	None available to homeowner.	See *RPD* 615.
Vinca—See Periwinkle.		
***Viola* (Violet)**—See Pansy.		
Zinnia Alternaria leaf spot or blight Other fungal leaf spots	2, 3, 4, 5, 11, 18.	See *RPD* 655.
Powdery mildew	2, 3, 6, 8, 11, 12, 16, 18, 19, 20, 21, 22, 23, 24.	See *RPD* 617.
Botrytis blight	2, 3, 4, 5, 9, 11, 21.	See *RPD* 623.
Fungal root and stem rot	9, 11.	See *RPD* 615.

[a]Refer to Table 7 for actual pesticide product names. Before using any product, carefully read its label to identify any varietal, environmental, or plant-stage interactions that may occur. Repeated, exclusive use of a product may lead to pesticide resistance and the loss of pest control. Whenever possible, alternate or mix products to reduce the development of pest resistance, as directed by the labels. See the *Illinois Commercial Landscape and Turfgrass Pest Management Handbook* (updated annually) for additional pesticide products available to commercial applicators.

Table 5. Disease Symptoms of Woody Ornamentals

General symptoms	Specific symptoms	Disease
Leaves		
Small to large, scattered spots in various sizes, shapes, and colors	Roundish spots; may contain dark, speck-sized fungal fruiting bodies.	Fungal leaf spot
	Spots may have dark margins or drop out (shot-hole).	Spot anthracnose Scab Shot-hole
	Black, shiny spots.	Tar spot
	Irregular dead areas in leaves.	Leaf blight or blotch
	Variously colored "blisters"; leaves often partly or entirely puffy, thickened, or curled.	Leaf curl or blister
Leaves spotted or blighted; later covered with dusty mold growth	Tan to gray, coarse mold.	Botrytis blight or gray mold
	White to light gray mold, powdery to mealy.	Powdery mildew
	Black mold, sooty or crusty.	Sooty mold
	Yellow, orange, reddish orange, reddish brown, chocolate brown, or black mold in raised pustules.	Rust
Leaves mottled light and dark green or yellow	Irregular mosaic pattern.	Mosaic
	Yellow-green or reddish brown rings, "oakleaf," "watermark," or line patterns.	Ringspot
Leaves wilt, wither, and die; may involve one or many branches or entire plant.	Discoloration in outer sapwood.	Wilt disease
	Foliage appears scorched by fire; twig tips curl downward to form "shepherd's crooks."	Fire blight
	Other possible causes include wood rot; black knot; drought or excess water; transplant shock; construction damage; change in soil grade; girdling roots; injury from insects, rodents, or other animals; pesticide or fertilizer damage; winter and frost injury; salt damage; lightning or fire injury; roots in septic tanks or sewer lines; or other mechanical injuries.	Miscellaneous diseases and injuries
Leaves "scorched" at margins and tips; often later between the veins		Leaf scorch (See also "Miscellaneous diseases and injuries," above.)

Table 5. Disease Symptoms of Woody Ornamentals (cont.)

General symptoms	Specific symptoms	Disease
Twigs, Branches, and Trunks Twigs and branches die back, usually starting at the tips; foliage commonly wilts, withers, and dies.	Discoloration in outer sapwood.	Wilt disease
	No discoloration in outer sapwood (See "**Roots,**" under specific symptoms.)	Root rot
	Foliage appears scorched by fire; twig tips curve downward.	Fire blight
	Sap flows down trunk and branches from wounds; becomes gray to white stain on bark.	Wetwood
	Definitely marked, often sunken, swollen, flattened, or targetlike areas (cankers) in bark and outer wood of twigs and branches.	Canker or dieback
Twigs and branches die back, usually starting at the tips; foliage commonly wilts, withers, and dies.	Wood in branches or trunk decays; bracket, shelf, or mushroom fungi may form on bark surface or trunk base.	Wood rot
	Other possible causes include injury from fertilizer, pesticide, or salt; drought or excess water; lightning or fire injury; transplant shock; winter injury; excess shade; construction damage; girdling roots; insect, rodent, or other animal injury; various types of mechanical damage; change in the soil grade; chlorosis.	Miscellaneous diseases and injuries
Greatly swollen areas on twigs, branches, or trunk	Galls on *Prunus* rough and black, or olive green and velvety in spring.	Black knot
	Roundish or spindle-shaped galls on branches or trunk; often covered with yellowish to orange dusty masses in spring or early summer.	Rust gall
	Rough, roundish, tumorlike galls, usually at or near the soil line or graft union.	Crown gall
	Large, irregular swellings anywhere on trunk or scaffold limbs of older trees.	Burr
Dense, brushy masses of stubby shoots form on branches.		Witches'-broom

Table 5. Disease Symptoms of Woody Ornamentals (cont.)

General symptoms	Specific symptoms	Disease
Roots Trees lose vigor, growth slows, foliage off-color; tops (crowns) may wilt and die back.	On roots, roundish, rough, tumorlike galls, up to several inches or more in diameter.	Crown gall
	Roots decay; feeder roots die back; mold growth under bark or over roots; usually shoestringlike black strands are evident.	Root rot
	Roots somewhat necrotic, lacking feeder roots; appear stunted or have small galls.	Nematodes (must be confirmed by soil or root analysis)
	Other possible causes include excess water; change in soil grade; construction damage; injury from fertilizer or pesticide; girdling roots; winter injury; salt, insect, or animal feeding; or wilt disease.	Miscellaneous diseases and injuries

Table 6. Products Labeled for Specific Woody Ornamentals

Plant and disease	Labeled pesticides[a]	Additional information
Acer—See Maple.		
Alder (Alnus) Powdery mildew Rust	6, 9, 11, 19, 29.	See *RPD* 617.
Almond—See Cherry.		
Amelanchier (Shadbush, Service berry, Juneberry) Cedar rusts	6.	See *RPD* 802.
Powdery mildew	6, 9, 11, 18, 19.	See *RPD* 617.
Fungal leaf spots	None available to homeowner.	See *RPD* 648.
Apple—See Crabapple.		
Apricot—See Cherry.		
Aralia Anthracnose Fungal leaf spots and blights	3, 11.	See *RPD* 641, 648.

[a]Refer to Table 7 for actual pesticide product names. Before using any product, carefully read its label to identify any varietal, environmental, or plant-stage interactions that may occur. Repeated, exclusive use of a product may lead to pesticide resistance and the loss of pest control. Whenever possible, alternate or mix products to reduce the development of pest resistance, as directed by the labels. See the *Illinois Commercial Landscape and Turfgrass Pest Management Handbook* (updated annually) for additional pesticide products available to commercial applicators.

Table 6. Products Labeled for Specific Woody Ornamentals (cont.)

Plant and disease	Labeled pesticides[a]	Additional information
Arborvitae *(Thuja)* Phomopsis needle and twig blight	4, 13.	See *RPD* 622.
Fungal root rot	11.	No *RPD*.
Ash (*Fraxinus,*** not Mountain-Ash)** Anthracnose Fungal leaf spots	2, 4, 11, 15, 20, 29.	See *RPD* 621, 648.
Powdery mildew Rust	4, 9, 11, 18, 29.	See *RPD* 617.
Aspen—See Poplar.		
Aucuba Fungal leaf spots	4.	See *RPD* 648.
Fungal root and crown rots	11.	No *RPD*.
Azalea—See *Rhododendron*.		
Barberry *(Berberis)* Bacterial leaf spot and twig blight	3, 13.	See *RPD* 648.
Fungal leaf spot and blotch Anthracnose	11.	See *RPD* 648, 621.
Powdery mildew Rust	6, 9, 11, 18, 19.	See *RPD* 617.
Basswood—See Linden.		
Beech *(Fagus)* Fungal leaf spot	11.	See *RPD* 648.
Powdery mildew	6, 9, 11, 19, 29.	See *RPD* 617.
Birch *(Betula)* Leaf blister *(Taphrina)*	None available to homeowner.	See *RPD* 663.
Anthracnose	11, 15, 29.	See *RPD* 621.
Rust Powdery mildew	4, 6, 9, 11, 18, 19 24, 29.	See *RPD* 617.
Bittersweet *(Celastrus)* Powdery mildew	6, 9, 11, 19.	See *RPD* 617.
Fungal leaf spots	11.	See *RPD* 648.

[a]Refer to Table 7 for actual pesticide product names. Before using any product, carefully read its label to identify any varietal, environmental, or plant-stage interactions that may occur. Repeated, exclusive use of a product may lead to pesticide resistance and the loss of pest control. Whenever possible, alternate or mix products to reduce the development of pest resistance, as directed by the labels. See the *Illinois Commercial Landscape and Turfgrass Pest Management Handbook* (updated annually) for additional pesticide products available to commercial applicators.

Table 6. Products Labeled for Specific Woody Ornamentals (cont.)

Plant and disease	Labeled pesticides[a]	Additional information
Boston Ivy—See Ivy.		
Boxelder—See Maple.		
Boxwood *(Buxus)*		
Canker or stem blight Fungal leaf spots and blights Anthracnose	3, 4, 11, 13, 29.	See *RPD* 621, 636, 648.
Phytophthora root rot	None available to homeowner.	No *RPD*.
Other root rots	11.	No *RPD*.
Buckeye—See Horsechestnut.		
Buckthorn *(Rhamnus)*		
Rust	18.	No *RPD*.
Fungal root rots	11.	No *RPD*.
Butternut—See Walnut.		
Buttonbush *(Cephalanthus)*		
Powdery mildew Rust	6, 9, 11, 19.	See *RPD* 617.
Fungal leaf spots	11.	See *RPD* 648.
Carissa		
Phytophthora root rot Pythium root rot	None available to homeowner.	No *RPD*.
Catalpa		
Powdery mildew	6, 9, 11, 19.	See *RPD* 617.
Fungal leaf spots	11.	See *RPD* 648.
Cherry, Peach, Nectarine, Plum, Almond, Apricot, Cherry-plum, Cherry-laurel *(nonbearing trees only)*		
Black knot	3.	See *RPD* 809.
Brown rot, blossom and twig blight Botrytis blight or gray mold	1, 2, 3, 4, 5, 6, 9, 11, 14, 20, 25, 28, 29, 30.	See *RPD* 804.

[a]Refer to Table 7 for actual pesticide product names. Before using any product, carefully read its label to identify any varietal, environmental, or plant-stage interactions that may occur. Repeated, exclusive use of a product may lead to pesticide resistance and the loss of pest control. Whenever possible, alternate or mix products to reduce the development of pest resistance, as directed by the labels. See the *Illinois Commercial Landscape and Turfgrass Pest Management Handbook* (updated annually) for additional pesticide products available to commercial applicators.

Table 6. Products Labeled for Specific Woody Ornamentals (cont.)

Plant and disease	Labeled pesticides[a]	Additional information
Cherry, Peach, Nectarine, Plum, Almond, Apricot, Cherry-plum, Cherry-laurel *(nonbearing trees only)* **(cont.)**		
Leaf blister or curl Plum pockets Witches'-broom	2, 3, 6, 13, 19, 20, 25, 29.	See *RPD* 623, 805.
Cherry leaf spot	1, 2, 3, 4, 6, 19, 20, 25, 28.	See *RPD* 800.
Powdery mildew	2, 6, 9, 11, 19, 24, 29.	See *RPD* 617.
Rust	4, 5, 6, 20, 24.	No *RPD*.
Scab Other fungal leaf spots	1, 2, 3, 4, 5, 6, 11, 20, 28, 30.	See *RPD* 811.
Bacterial shot-hole	3.	See *RPD* 810.
Phytophthora collar and root rot	None available to homeowner.	No *RPD*.
Chestnut—See Horsechestnut.		
Cotoneaster Fire blight	21.	See *RPD* 801.
Scab	4, 21.	See *RPD* 803.
Fungal leaf spots Botrytis blight	3, 4, 9, 11, 21.	See *RPD* 623, 648.
Fungal root rot	11.	No *RPD*
Cottonwood—See Poplar.		
Crabapple, Flowering crab, Apple, Pear *(nonbearing trees only)* Cedar rusts (apple, hawthorn, and quince)	2, 4, 5, 6, 11, 18, 20, 24.	See *RPD* 802.
Scab Fungal leaf spots and fruit rots Sooty blotch and flyspeck	1, 2, 3, 4, 5, 6, 9, 11, 13, 19, 20, 21, 25, 28, 29, 30.	See *RPD* 803, 814, 815.
Fire blight	3, 4, 10, 15, 21.	See *RPD* 801.

[a]Refer to Table 7 for actual pesticide product names. Before using any product, carefully read its label to identify any varietal, environmental, or plant-stage interactions that may occur. Repeated, exclusive use of a product may lead to pesticide resistance and the loss of pest control. Whenever possible, alternate or mix products to reduce the development of pest resistance, as directed by the labels. See the *Illinois Commercial Landscape and Turfgrass Pest Management Handbook* (updated annually) for additional pesticide products available to commercial applicators.

Table 6. Products Labeled for Specific Woody Ornamentals (cont.)

Plant and disease	Labeled pesticides[a]	Additional information
Crabapple, Flowering crab, Apple, Pear *(nonbearing trees only)* **(cont.)**		
Powdery mildew	1, 3, 6, 9, 11, 18, 19, 24, 29.	See *RPD* 816.
Phytophthora crown or collar root rot	3.	See *RPD* 812.
Currant, Alpine *(Ribes)*		
Anthracnose Fungal leaf spots	3, 6, 11, 25.	See *RPD* 621, 648.
Powdery mildew	6, 9, 11, 19, 29.	See *RPD* 617.
Dogwood *(Cornus)*		
Fungal leaf spots Leaf blotch Anthracnose Spot anthracnose Flower and leaf blights	2, 3, 4, 5, 11, 13, 15, 17, 20.	See *RPD* 621, 648.
Powdery mildew	6, 9, 11, 18, 19, 21.	See *RPD* 617.
Phytophthora stem and root rot Phythium root rot	None available to homeowner.	No *RPD*
Elm *(Ulmus)*		
Anthracnose Black leaf spot and other fungal leaf spots Twig blight	4, 11, 13, 15, 25, 29.	See *RPD* 621.
Powdery mildew	9, 11, 18, 19, 29.	See *RPD* 617.
Elm yellows	None available.	See *RPD* 660.
Dutch elm disease	Sanitation measures and prevention.	The fungus is spread via bark beetles, root grafts, and contaminated pruning tools. Root grafting occurs between trees within 25 to 50 feet of one another. Trenching to a depth of 3 feet between trees temporarily disrupts root grafting. Remove and burn (or de-bark) the infested tree and stump as soon as possible to eliminate it as a disease source. See *RPD* 647.

[a]Refer to Table 7 for actual pesticide product names. Before using any product, carefully read its label to identify any varietal, environmental, or plant-stage interactions that may occur. Repeated, exclusive use of a product may lead to pesticide resistance and the loss of pest control. Whenever possible, alternate or mix products to reduce the development of pest resistance, as directed by the labels. See the *Illinois Commercial Landscape and Turfgrass Pest Management Handbook* (updated annually) for additional pesticide products available to commercial applicators.

Table 6. Products Labeled for Specific Woody Ornamentals (cont.)

Plant and disease	Labeled pesticides[a]	Additional information
Euonymus Fungal leaf spots Anthracnose Scab Botrytis blight	2, 3, 4, 9, 11, 20.	See *RPD* 621, 623, 648.
Powdery mildew	6, 9, 11, 18, 19, 22, 23, 24.	See *RPD* 617.
Fungal root and crown rot	11.	No *RPD*.
Evergreens—See Fir, Juniper, Pine, Yew.		
Fir, Douglas—See Pine.		
Fir (*Abies*, not Douglas fir) Needle and twig blights Leaf casts	4.	No *RPD*.
Botrytis blight	9, 11.	See *RPD* 623.
Rust	4, 6, 18.	No *RPD*.
Fungal root rot	11.	No *RPD*.
Firethorn—See *Pyracantha*.		
Forsythia Fungal leaf spots	11.	See *RPD* 648.
Hawthorn, Red haw (*Crataegus*) Scab Fungal leaf spots and blights	2, 3, 4, 11, 15.	See *RPD* 637.
Cedar rusts	2, 4, 6, 15, 18.	See *RPD* 802.
Fire blight	None available to homeowner.	See *RPD* 801.
Powdery mildew	6, 9, 11, 18, 19, 29.	See *RPD* 617.
Hemlock (*Tsuga*) Phythophthora root rot	None available to homeowner.	No *RPD*.
Rust	18.	No *RPD*.

[a]Refer to Table 7 for actual pesticide product names. Before using any product, carefully read its label to identify any varietal, environmental, or plant-stage interactions that may occur. Repeated, exclusive use of a product may lead to pesticide resistance and the loss of pest control. Whenever possible, alternate or mix products to reduce the development of pest resistance, as directed by the labels. See the *Illinois Commercial Landscape and Turfgrass Pest Management Handbook* (updated annually) for additional pesticide products available to commercial applicators.

Table 6. Products Labeled for Specific Woody Ornamentals (cont.)

Plant and disease	Labeled pesticides[a]	Additional information
Hickory (*Carya*, not Pecan) Anthracnose Fungal leaf spot or blotch Scab Spot anthracnose	4, 11, 29.	See *RPD* 621, 648.
Holly (*Ilex*) Fungal leaf spots, blights Tar spot Anthracnose Spot anthrascnose	2, 4, 11.	See *RPD* 621, 648.
Rizoctonia leaf blight	2, 20.	No *RPD*
Powdery mildew	6, 11, 18, 19, 24.	See *RPD* 617.
Fungal root rots	11.	No *RPD*
Honeysuckle (*Lonicera*) Herpobasidium leaf blight	4.	No *RPD*
Fungal leaf spots	11.	See *RPD* 648.
Powdery mildew	6, 11, 19.	See *RPD* 617.
Fungal root and crown rot	11.	No *RPD*
Horsechestnut, Buckeye (*Aeculus*) Leaf blotch Fungal leaf spot or blotch Anthracnose Spot anthracnose	2, 4, 11, 15, 20, 29.	See *RPD* 621, 648.
Powdery mildew	6, 9, 11, 18, 19, 29.	See *RPD* 617.
Hydrangea Fungal leaf spots Rust	2, 4, 6, 11, 20.	See *RPD* 648.
Botrytis leaf and flower blight or gray mold	2, 4, 5, 9, 11, 17.	See *RPD* 623.
Powdery mildew	6, 9, 11. 19.	See *RPD* 617.
Fungal root and stem rot	11.	No *RPD*.

[a]Refer to Table 7 for actual pesticide product names. Before using any product, carefully read its label to identify any varietal, environmental, or plant-stage interactions that may occur. Repeated, exclusive use of a product may lead to pesticide resistance and the loss of pest control. Whenever possible, alternate or mix products to reduce the development of pest resistance, as directed by the labels. See the *Illinois Commercial Landscape and Turfgrass Pest Management Handbook* (updated annually) for additional pesticide products available to commercial applicators.

Table 6. Products Labeled for Specific Woody Ornamentals (cont.)

Plant and disease	Labeled pesticides[a]	Additional information
Ivy, Boston, and Virginia creeper *(Parthenocissus)*		
Powdery mildew	6, 9, 11, 24.	See *RPD* 617.
Botrytis blight	9, 13.	See *RPD* 623.
Fungal leaf spots	3, 4, 11, 13.	See *RPD* 648.
Ivy, English—See Table 4.		
Juneberry—See *Amelanchier.*		
Juniper, Redcedar *(Juniperus)*		
Cedar rusts	3, 4, 6, 18, 24.	See *RPD* 802.
Phomopsis twig blight	4, 11, 13.	See *RPD* 622.
Cercospora needle blight	4.	No *RPD.*
Botrytis blight	9, 11.	See *RPD* 623.
Fungal root rots	11.	No *RPD.*
Laurel, Cherry—See Cherry.		
Ligustrum—See Privet.		
Leucothoe		
Fungal leaf spots	11, 18.	See *RPD* 648.
Fungal root and crown rot	11.	No *RPD.*
Lilac *(Syringa)*		
Powdery mildew	2, 6, 9, 11, 15, 18, 19, 22, 23, 29.	See *RPD* 617.
Fungal leaf spots and blights	3, 11, 13, 29.	See *RPD* 648.
Bacterial leaf spots and blights	2, 13, 21.	No *RPD.*
Linden, Basswood *(Tilia)*		
Anthracnose Fungal leaf spots Leaf blight Spot anthracnose	3, 11, 13, 15, 25, 29.	See *RPD* 621, 648.
Powdery mildew	6, 9, 11, 19, 29.	See *RPD* 617.

[a]Refer to Table 7 for actual pesticide product names. Before using any product, carefully read its label to identify any varietal, environmental, or plant-stage interactions that may occur. Repeated, exclusive use of a product may lead to pesticide resistance and the loss of pest control. Whenever possible, alternate or mix products to reduce the development of pest resistance, as directed by the labels. See the *Illinois Commercial Landscape and Turfgrass Pest Management Handbook* (updated annually) for additional pesticide products available to commercial applicators.

Table 6. Products Labeled for Specific Woody Ornamentals (cont.)

Plant and disease	Labeled pesticides[a]	Additional information
Magnolia		
Powdery mildew	6, 9, 11, 19.	See _RPD_ 617.
Fungal leaf spots and blights	2, 3, 4, 9, 11.	See _RPD_ 648.
Bacterial leaf spots	3, 4.	No _RPD_.
Phytophthora or Pythium root rot	None available to homeowner.	No _RPD_.
Maple, Boxelder (_Acer_)		
Anthracnose	2, 3, 4, 11, 13, 15, 25, 29.	
Fungal leaf spots		See _RPD_ 621, 648, 663.
Leaf blight or blotch		
Leaf scab		
Tar spot		
Leaf blister		
Powdery mildew	6, 9, 11, 18, 19, 24, 29.	See _RPD_ 617.
Fungal root rots	11.	No _RPD_.
Mock-Orange (_Maclura pomifera_)		
Powdery mildew	6, 9, 11, 18, 19.	See _RPD_ 617.
Rust		
Mountain-Ash (_Sorbus_)		
Leaf blight and scab	2, 4, 11, 21.	
Fungal leaf spots		See _RPD_ 648.
Rusts	4, 6.	No _RPD_.
Fire blight	21.	See _RPD_ 801.
Mulberry (_Morus_)		
Bacterial blight or leaf spot	3.	See _RPD_ 648.
Fungal leaf spots and blights	9, 11.	See _RPD_ 648.
Powdery mildew	6, 9, 11, 19.	See _RPD_ 617.
Nectarine—See Cherry.		

[a] Refer to Table 7 for actual pesticide product names. Before using any product, carefully read its label to identify any varietal, environmental, or plant-stage interactions that may occur. Repeated, exclusive use of a product may lead to pesticide resistance and the loss of pest control. Whenever possible, alternate or mix products to reduce the development of pest resistance, as directed by the labels. See the _Illinois Commercial Landscape and Turfgrass Pest Management Handbook_ (updated annually) for additional pesticide products available to commercial applicators.

Table 6. Products Labeled for Specific Woody Ornamentals (cont.)

Plant and disease	Labeled pesticides[a]	Additional information
Oak (*Quercus*) Anthracnose (leaf-blight stage only) Fungal leaf spots and blights Leaf blotch Taphrina leaf blister	2, 3, 4, 11, 13, 15, 20, 21, 25, 29.	See *RPD* 621, 648, 663.
Powdery mildew	6, 9, 11, 18, 19, 24, 29.	See *RPD* 617.
Oak wilt	Sanitation measures and prevention.	The fungus is spread via root grafts and insects that feed on fresh wounds. Prune oaks only during late fall or when dormant. Root grafting occurs between some oak species within 25 to 50 feet of one another. Trenching to a depth of 3 feet between trees temporarily disrupts root grafting. Remove and burn (or de-bark) the infested tree and stump as soon as possible to eliminate it as a disease source. See *RPD* 618.
Peach—See Cherry.		
Pear—See Crabapple.		
Pecan (*Carya illinoensis*, nonbearing trees only) Scab Fungal leaf spots, blotch, and scorch Spot anthracnose Anthracnose Sooty mold	3, 11, 15, 29.	See *RPD* 621, 648.
Powdery mildew	6, 9, 11, 19, 29.	See *RPD* 617.
Pine, Spruce, Douglas fir Dothistroma needle blight	3.	Seer *RPD* 624.
Scirrhia brown spot and needle blight (pines) Rhizosphaera needle cast (spruces) Sirococcus tip bight	2, 3, 4, 11, 13, 18, 20.	See *RPD* 624.
Lophodermium and Cyclaneusma needle cast (pines)	2, 4, 20.	See *RPD* 624.

[a]Refer to Table 7 for actual pesticide product names. Before using any product, carefully read its label to identify any varietal, environmental, or plant-stage interactions that may occur. Repeated, exclusive use of a product may lead to pesticide resistance and the loss of pest control. Whenever possible, alternate or mix products to reduce the development of pest resistance, as directed by the labels. See the *Illinois Commercial Landscape and Turfgrass Pest Management Handbook* (updated annually) for additional pesticide products available to commercial applicators.

Table 6. Products Labeled for Specific Woody Ornamentals (cont.)

Plant and disease	Labeled pesticides[a]	Additional information
Pine, Spruce, Douglas fir (cont.)		
Sphaeropsis (Diplodia) tip blight or dieback	2, 3, 4, 11, 20, 21.	See *RPD* 625.
Rhabdocline needle cast (Douglas fir)		
Scleroderris or Gremmeniella canker (pines)	2, 4, 20.	No *RPD*.
Swiss needle cast (Douglas fir)		
Rust	4, 6, 18.	No *RPD*.
Pinewood nematode	None available to homeowner.	Remove and destroy the infested tree and other dead pines in the area immediately. Do not store infested wood; it will serve as a source of future infestations. The pinewood nematode is not known to infest or survive in below-ground plant parts. See *RPD* 1104.
Cylindrocladium blight and root rot	4, 9, 11.	No *RPD*.
Botrytis seedling blight	2, 4, 9.	See *RPD* 623.
Phoma twig blight		
Rhizoctonia needle blight	None available to homeowner.	No *RPD*.
Damping-off	11.	No *RPD*.
Fungal root rot		
Pittosporum		
Fungal leaf spots	4, 9, 11.	See *RPD* 623, 648.
Botrytis bight		
Fungal root and crown rot	11.	No *RPD*.
Planetree—See Sycamore.		
Plum—See Cherry.		
Poplar, Aspen, Cottonwood (*Populus*)		
Leaf rusts	2, 3, 4, 6, 11, 15, 20, 24, 29.	See *RPD* 605, 621, 648.
Anthracnose		
Other fungal leaf spots		

[a]Refer to Table 7 for actual pesticide product names. Before using any product, carefully read its label to identify any varietal, environmental, or plant-stage interactions that may occur. Repeated, exclusive use of a product may lead to pesticide resistance and the loss of pest control. Whenever possible, alternate or mix products to reduce the development of pest resistance, as directed by the labels. See the *Illinois Commercial Landscape and Turfgrass Pest Management Handbook* (updated annually) for additional pesticide products available to commercial applicators.

Table 6. Products Labeled for Specific Woody Ornamentals (cont.)

Plant and disease	Labeled pesticides[a]	Additional information
Poplar, Aspen, Cottonwood *(Populus)* **(cont.)**		
Yellow leaf blister *(Taphrina)*	None available to homeowner.	See *RPD* 663.
Powdery mildew	6, 9, 11, 18, 19, 24, 29.	See *RPD* 617.
Rust	18, 22.	No *RPD*.
Privet *(Ligustrum)*		
Anthracnose Fungal leaf spots Twig blight	2, 4, 9, 11, 18, 20.	See *RPD* 621, 648.
Powdery mildew	6, 9, 11, 18, 19.	See *RPD* 617.
Damping-off Fungal root and stem rots	11.	No *RPD*.
Pyracantha **(Firethorn)**		
Fire blight	3, 4, 10, 21.	See *RPD* 801.
Fungal leaf spots	2, 4, 11.	See *RPD* 648.
Powdery mildew	6, 9, 11, 18, 19, 24.	See *RPD* 617.
Scab	2, 3, 4, 9, 11, 20, 21, 24.	See *RPD* 638.
Quince *(Cydonia)*		
Fire blight	3.	See *RPD* 801.
Brown rot blossom blight	2, 20.	See *RPD* 804.
Rust Scab Fungal leaf spots	6, 11, 20.	See *RPD* 648, 802.
Redbud *(Cercis)*		
Cercospora and other fungal leaf spots	9, 11.	See *RPD* 648.
Redcedar—See Juniper.		
Red haw—See Hawthorn.		

[a]Refer to Table 7 for actual pesticide product names. Before using any product, carefully read its label to identify any varietal, environmental, or plant-stage interactions that may occur. Repeated, exclusive use of a product may lead to pesticide resistance and the loss of pest control. Whenever possible, alternate or mix products to reduce the development of pest resistance, as directed by the labels. See the *Illinois Commercial Landscape and Turfgrass Pest Management Handbook* (updated annually) for additional pesticide products available to commercial applicators.

Table 6. Products Labeled for Specific Woody Ornamentals (cont.)

Plant and disease	Labeled pesticides[a]	Additional information
Rhodendron (Azalea)		
Ovulinia petal or flower blight of azalea	1, 2, 4, 11, 18, 20, 22.	No *RPD*.
Powdery mildew	3, 4, 6, 9, 11, 18, 19, 22, 24.	See *RPD* 617.
Fungal leaf spots Rusts Leaf, flower, and stem galls Botrytis blight	2, 3, 4, 5, 6, 9, 11, 17, 21, 24.	See *RPD* 623, 639, 648.
Bud and twig blight Dieback	2, 3, 4, 20.	No *RPD*.
Root and crown rot and dieback (*Phytophthora*)	None available to homeowner.	See *RPD* 664.
Cutting rot or dieback Cylindrocladium root rot	1, 4, 9, 11, 14, 21.	No *RPD*.
Other fungal root rots	21.	No *RPD*.
Rose *(Rosa)*		
Botrytis bud, blossom, and cane blight	1, 2, 4, 9, 11, 12, 16, 20, 21, 26, 27.	See *RPD* 623.
Black spot Other cane blights Cankers Spot anthracnose Anthracnose Other fungal leaf spots Rusts	1, 2, 3, 4, 5, 6, 8, 9, 11, 12, 14, 15, 16, 17, 19, 20, 21, 22, 23, 24, 26, 27.	See *RPD* 610, 621, 626, 630, 648.
Downy mildew	4.	See *RPD* 611.
Powdery mildew	3, 4, 6, 9, 11, 15, 18, 19, 21, 22, 23, 24, 26, 27, 29.	See *RPD* 617.
Russian-olive *(Elaegnus)*		
Fungal leaf spots	11, 18, 29.	See *RPD* 648.
Rust	18.	No *RPD*.
Serviceberry, Shadbush— See *Amelanchier.*		

[a]Refer to Table 7 for actual pesticide product names. Before using any product, carefully read its label to identify any varietal, environmental, or plant-stage interactions that may occur. Repeated, exclusive use of a product may lead to pesticide resistance and the loss of pest control. Whenever possible, alternate or mix products to reduce the development of pest resistance, as directed by the labels. See the *Illinois Commercial Landscape and Turfgrass Pest Management Handbook* (updated annually) for additional pesticide products available to commercial applicators.

Table 6. Products Labeled for Specific Woody Ornamentals (cont.)

Plant and disease	Labeled pesticides[a]	Additional information
Spiraea *(Spirea)* Powdery mildew	6, 9, 11, 18, 19, 24.	See *RPD* 617.
Botrytis blight	None available to homeowner.	See *RPD* 623.
Fungal leaf spots	2.	See *RPD* 648.
Spruce—See Pine.		
Sumac *(Rhus)* Fungal leaf spots	11.	See *RPD* 648.
Sycamore, Planetree *(Plantanus)* Anthracnose (leaf-blight stage only) Fungal leaf spots and blights Rust	2, 3, 4, 11, 13, 15, 20, 21, 22, 29.	See *RPD* 621, 648.
Powdery mildew	6, 9, 11, 18, 19, 22, 24, 29.	See *RPD* 617.
Taxus—See Yew.		
Thuja—See Arborvitae.		
Tuliptree *(Liriodendron)* Anthracnose Fungal leaf spots	11, 15, 29.	See *RPD* 621, 648.
Powdery mildew	6, 9, 11, 19, 29.	See *RPD* 617.
Viburnum Fungal leaf spots	3, 4, 11.	See *RPD* 641.
Powdery mildew	2, 6, 9, 11, 19, 20, 24.	See *RPD* 617.
Downy mildew	4.	No *RPD*.
Rust	4, 18, 24.	No *RPD*.
Virginia creeper—See Ivy.		
Walnut, Butternut *(Jugulans)* Anthracnose Yellow leaf blotch Fungal leaf spots or blights	2, 4, 11, 15, 29.	See *RPD* 600, 621.

[a]Refer to Table 7 for actual pesticide product names. Before using any product, carefully read its label to identify any varietal, environmental, or plant-stage interactions that may occur. Repeated, exclusive use of a product may lead to pesticide resistance and the loss of pest control. Whenever possible, alternate or mix products to reduce the development of pest resistance, as directed by the labels. See the *Illinois Commercial Landscape and Turfgrass Pest Management Handbook* (updated annually) for additional pesticide products available to commercial applicators.

Table 6. Products Labeled for Specific Woody Ornamentals (cont.)

Plant and disease	Labeled pesticides[a]	Additional information
Walnut, Butternut *(Jugulans)* **(cont.)**		
Bacterial blight (of Persian or English walnut)	3, 4.	No *RPD*.
Powdery mildew	6, 9, 11, 18, 19, 29.	See *RPD* 617.
Willow *(Salix)*		
Tar spot Leaf blight Scab Black canker Spot anthracnose	3, 4, 11, 13, 15, 29.	No *RPD*.
Powdery mildew Rust	4, 6, 9, 11, 18, 19, 24, 29.	See *RPD* 605, 617.
Witchhazel *(Hamamelis)*		
Powdery mildew	6, 9, 11, 19.	See *RPD* 617.
Fungal leaf spots	11.	See *RPD* 648.
Yew (Taxus)		
Twig blight *(Phomposis)*	3, 13.	See *RPD* 622.
Phytophthora root rot	None available to homeowner.	No *RPD*.
Site disinfestation		
Nematodes Soilborne fungi	None available to homeowner.	Refer to the *Illinois Commercial Landscape and Turfgrass Pest Management Handbook* for what may be applied by certified pesticide applicators.

[a]Refer to Table 7 for actual pesticide product names. Before using any product, carefully read its label to identify any varietal, environmental, or plant-stage interactions that may occur. Repeated, exclusive use of a product may lead to pesticide resistance and the loss of pest control. Whenever possible, alternate or mix products to reduce the development of pest resistance, as directed by the labels. See the *Illinois Commercial Landscape and Turfgrass Pest Management Handbook* (updated annually) for additional pesticide products available to commercial applicators.

Table 7. Coded Pesticide Product List for Tables 2, 4, and 6

Code	Trade name	Common name
1	Many products	captan
2	Many products	chlorothalonil
3	Many products	copper
4	Many products	mancozeb (= maneb + Zn)
5	Many products	maneb
6	Many products	sulfur
7	Many products	thiram
8	Black Leaf Lawn & Garden	chlorothalonil
9	Black Leaf Rose & Ornamental	thiophanate-methyl
10	Ferti-lome Fire Blight Spray	streptomycin sulfate
11	Ferti-lome Halt	thiophanate-methyl
12	Ferti-lome Liquid Fungicide	chlorothalonil
13	Hi-Yield Bordeaux Mix	copper sulfate
14	Hi-Yield Captan	captan
15	Hi-Yield Consan 20	ammonium chlorides
16	Hi-Yield Daconil	chlorothalonil
17	Hi-Yield Maneb Lawn & Garen	maneb
18	Monterey Bayleton	triadimefon
19	Ortho Dormant Disease Control Lime-Sulfur Spray	calcium polysulfides
20	Ortho Multi-Purpose Fungicide Daconil 2787	chlorothalonil
21	Phyton 27	copper sulfate pentahydrate
22	RosePride Funginex Rose & Shrub Disease Control	triforine
23	RosePride Orthenex Rose & Shrub Disease Control	triforine + acephate* + hexakis*
24	RosePride Orthenex Rose & Shrub Disease Control-1	triforine + acephate* + resmethrin*
25	Many products	bordeaux
26	Ferti-lome Rose Spray	chlorothalonil + diazinon*
27	Ferti-lome Triple Action	chlorothalonil + diazinon*
28	Ferti-lome Fruit Tree Spray	captan + malathion*
29	Hi-Yield Lime Sulfur	calcium polysulfides
30	Ortho Home Orchard Spray	captan + malathion* + methoxychlor*

NOTE: Before using any product, carefully read its label to identify any varietal, environmental, or plant-stage interactions that may occur. Repeated, exclusive use of a product may lead to pesticide resistance and the loss of pest control. Whenever possible, alternate or mix products to reduce the development of pest resistance, as directed by the labels. See the *Illinois Commercial Landscape and Turfgrass Pest Management Handbook* (updated annually) for additional pesticide products available to commercial applicators.
*Compounds marked with an asterisk are insecticides.

Authors

N. Pataky and B. Paulsrud
Department of Crop Sciences

CHAPTER TWO

Controlling Weeds in Home Lawns

1 *Dens Leonis.*
Dandelion.

Weed Control in Home Lawns

Weeds are plants growing where they are not wanted. Weeds are usually controlled in home lawns because they distract from the overall appearance of the turf. High-quality lawns normally are judged by their uniformity. Uniformity is the combined visual effects of lawn grass leaf width (texture), color, density, and growth habit. Weeds often have different leaf shapes, sizes, flowers, colors, or growth habits than lawn grasses and, thus, reduce uniformity within a turf area. Several turfgrasses, such as tall fescue or creeping bentgrass, may be weeds when growing in Kentucky bluegrass or fine-fescue turf areas because these grasses reduce the uniformity of the turf.

Weed Life Cycles

Weeds usually have one of three life cycles: annual, biennial, or perennial.

Annual weeds live for a single season. There are two types of annuals, and both reproduce by seeds. Cool-season annuals (also known as winter annuals) germinate in late summer or fall, are dormant during the winter, flower in spring or early summer, and then die. Chickweed *(Stellaria media)* and henbit *(Lamium amplexicaule)* are examples of cool-season annual weeds. Warm-season annuals (also known as summer annuals) germinate during spring or summer, flower, and die at the end of that growing season. Crabgrass *(Digitaria* spp.), goosegrass *(Eleusine indica)*, spurge *(Euphorbia supina)*, knotweed *(Polygonum aviculare)*, and yellow foxtail *(Setaria glauca)* are examples of warm-season annual weeds.

Biennial weeds live for two seasons. During the first growing season, these weeds remain in a vegetative phase. Following a cold treatment (vernalization), biennial weeds bolt, flower, set seed, and die during the second growing season. Wild carrot *(Daucus carota)* and bull thistle *(Cirsium vulgare)* are examples of biennial weeds in turf.

Perennial weeds live for multiple seasons and flower more than once. Perennial structures (rhizomes, stolons, crowns, entire plants, nutlets, or roots) survive

The information in this chapter is provided for educational purposes only. Product trade names have been used for clarity, but reference to trade names does not imply endorsement by the University of Illinois; discrimination is not intended against any product. The reader is urged to exercise caution in making purchases or evaluating product information.

Label registrations can change at any time. Thus the recommendations in this chapter may become invalid. The user must read carefully the entire, most recent label and follow all directions and restrictions. Purchase only enough pesticide for the current growing season.

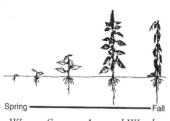

Spring ——————— Fall

Warm-Season Annual Weeds

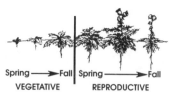

Spring ——▶ Fall   Spring ——▶ Fall
VEGETATIVE   REPRODUCTIVE

Biennial Weeds

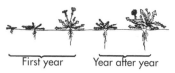

First year   Year after year

Perennial Weeds

from year to year. Wild garlic *(Allium vineale)*, yellow nutsedge *(Cyperus esculentus)*, quackgrass *(Elytrigia repens)*, ground ivy *(Glechoma hederacea)*, and violet *(Viola* spp.) are examples of perennial weeds.

Lawn Weed Control

There are several lawn weed control methods homeowners can employ. The first method is weed prevention, the second is the use of environmental and cultural management, and the third is the use of chemical weed controls.

Prevention

When planting turfgrasses, it is important to use soil, seed, sod, plugs, or sprigs that are as free of weeds as possible. If you are bringing in soil for landscape applications, attempt to buy soil that does not contain weed seeds or vegetative plant parts that may develop into future weed problems. Inspect seed labels to determine the quantity of weed or crop seed within the seed. Avoid planting annual ryegrass in any permanent turf setting; although it is generally short-lived, it may persist as a weed grass for more than one growing season. Examine sod, plugs, or sprigs for the presence of weeds before purchase. In general, purchase and use high-quality soil, seed, sod, plugs, or sprigs at the time of lawn establishment. The high quality may be somewhat more costly in the short run but provides an attractive lawn with fewer weeds over the long run.

Reducing weed spread from areas adjacent to established turf also can help prevent weed infestations. Mowing weeds before they flower can reduce seed movement into turf areas.

Environmental and Cultural Management

Another defense against weed infestations in turfgrass is to produce a dense stand of healthy turf. Quality turf can compete well with weeds. It is best achieved by providing a good growing environment and by properly preparing planting soils, planting high-quality turfgrasses suitable for the given situation, and using proper cultural practices (mowing, watering, fertilizing, and cultivating).

Excessive traffic physically damages turf and also compacts soil; thin turf, which can result, is prone to weed invasion. Perennial ryegrass and tall fescues have the ability to tolerate wear better than most other cool-season grasses. Where appropriate, use these grasses in high-traffic areas. Compaction reduces the quantity of large, gas-containing pore spaces in soils. Some weeds (for example, goosegrass and knotweed) are more tolerant of low-oxygen conditions in soil than are most turfgrasses. Cultivate these areas so that the turf can better compete with weeds.

Along with compacted soils, other unfavorable growth environments also can create growing conditions in which weeds are better adapted than turf. Shade that reduces light quantity and quality favors weeds (for example, creeping Charlie and common chickweed) rather than turf. Prune or remove trees to allow more light to reach the growing area. This also can increase air movement and decrease disease problems. Soils that are excessively wet or dry also create environments in which weeds often grow better than does turf. If possible, provide external and internal drainage to remove excess water from the turf root zone. Also, supplemental irrigation may be used in dry periods. In general, try to create growing environments that favor your lawn instead of weeds.

Cultural defense against turfgrass pests begins with the proper preparation of planting soils and the planting of selected turfgrass cultivars. Proper planting of turfgrasses includes planting bed preparation, timing, and use of high-quality,

Table 1. Recommended Turfgrass Planting Combinations for Specific Midwest Sites and Applications

Setting	Turfgrass
Full sun	Kentucky bluegrass blend (3 or more Kentucky bluegrass cultivars) **OR** >80% Kentucky bluegrass/perennial ryegrass **OR** tall fescue blend (3 or more tall fescue cultivars) **OR** bermudagrass (southern portion of Midwest) **OR** buffalograss (very-low-maintenance areas) **OR** zoysiagrass (southern portion of Midwest)
Dry shade	30–50% blend of shade-tolerant Kentucky bluegrasses + 50–70% fine-leaf fescues **OR** tall fescue blend OR zoysiagrass (southern portion of Midwest)
Wet shade	70% or more rough bluegrass + remainder in blend of shade-tolerant Kentucky bluegrasses

adequate seed, sod, plugs, or stolons. It is important to pay particular attention to soil drainage, moisture retention, fertility, and pH. A properly prepared planting bed meets a turf's growth demand; this can reduce future problems associated with soils that are too wet or dry, infertile, prone to compaction, full of debris, or too acidic or alkaline.

When selecting turfgrasses, it is important to consider the turf's use, its growth environment, its desired appearance, the management it will receive, and its resistance to pests. Plant high-quality turfgrasses that are most likely to give you the outcome you desire. We recommend that mixes (combinations of two or more species of turfgrass) and/or blends (combinations of two or more cultivars of the same species) be planted to reduce overall turfgrass disease potential and provide grasses capable of tolerating varied sites (Table 1).

Following turfgrass planting and selection, mowing, irrigating, fertilizing, and cultivating can be used to reduce pest problems. Proper mowing is critical to turfgrass health and appearance because turfgrasses that are mowed too short become open, inviting weed invasion. They also may develop inadequate root systems, which allow plants to succumb more readily to insect and disease pests. If turfgrasses are allowed to grow too tall, they can appear unkempt and coarse-

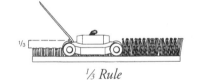

⅓ Rule

Table 2. Suggested Mowing Heights (in Inches) for Commonly Used Turfgrass Species

Turf species	Mowing height (in inches)
Buffalograss	2 to 3
Creeping bentgrass	¼ to ¾
Fine-leaf fescue	2 to 3
Kentucky bluegrass	2 to 3
Perennial ryegrass	2 to 3
Tall fescue	2 to 3
Zoysiagrass	1 to 1½

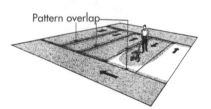

Proper watering means watering deeply to the depth of the root system.

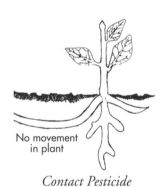

Pattern overlap

Dry Spreader Application

No movement in plant

Contact Pesticide

Rhizome

Systemic Pesticide

textured; turfgrass playability on athletic fields can also be affected. Basic mowing recommendations include frequent mowing at the tallest height recommended for the specific turf appearance and use (Table 2).

Irrigating turfgrasses is also important. Overwatered turf may grow too rapidly, develop shallow root systems, and be prone to invasions of weeds, insects, and diseases. Underirrigated turf may become open and sparse, develop a poor appearance, and allow weed invasions. Under most circumstances, water deeply and infrequently, to the depth of the root system. To maintain green, actively growing turfgrass throughout the entire season, supply 1 to 1½ inches of water per week from natural or artificial sources.

Fertilizers maintain turfgrass density, vigor, and color. Applying large amounts of nitrogen, however, can result in turfgrasses that are lush and prone to many diseases. Inadequate nitrogen fertilization leads to open turf that is readily invaded by weeds. If other minerals in the soil—especially potassium, phosphorus, iron, and sulfur—are present in adequate amounts, turf color, disease resistance, and stress tolerance can be improved. Conduct soil tests and supply these elements as recommended by test results. Lacking test results, supply a complete fertilizer in appropriate amounts and timing to capitalize on periods of active turfgrass growth.

Cultivation activities include core aerification, slicing, and vertical mowing. These activities can reduce thatch and prepare turf for overseeding. Core aerification is also useful for reducing soil compaction. Conduct cultivation activities during periods of active growth, when turfgrasses are best able to recover from these practices.

See other turfgrass management publications available from ACES/ITCS Product Sales and Distribution and from the Department of Natural Resources and Environmental Sciences at the University of Illinois.

Chemical Weed Controls

Although proper turfgrass planting, selection, and culture should result in adequate pest control, at times the intelligent selection and use of chemical weed controls (herbicides) may be necessary to control turf weeds. Herbicides should be used only after weed prevention activities and proper culture have failed to produce the desired quality of turf. Avoid using herbicides as a quick fix while mismanaging your lawn.

For the most efficient weed control and safest use, be sure to read, understand, and follow all label directions before mixing and using any herbicide. A few minutes spent studying the information on the label may prevent misuse and needless accidents.

Herbicides control one or more plant species. They may be classified into one of three types (contact, systemic, or soil sterilant), depending upon the nature of their activity on plants.

Contact herbicides kill plant parts covered by the chemical. *Systemic herbicides,* absorbed by plant organs and translocated throughout the plant, may be either *selective,* killing certain weeds without injuring desirable grasses, or *nonselective,* controlling all vegetation.

Glyphosate, a nonselective herbicide, is useful in renovating turfs infested with extensive populations of annual weeds. Glyphosate is also used to kill perennial weedy grasses, such as quackgrass, that cannot be controlled by selective herbicides. Because glyphosate has no residual soil activity, treated areas may be reseeded soon after application. Mecoprop is a selective herbicide used to control broadleaved weeds in turf.

Soil sterilants are chemicals that render the soil toxic to all plant life. How long the soil remains sterile depends upon the material used, the rate of application, and the prevailing environmental conditions that affect decomposition of the herbicide in the soil. *Soil sterilants have no place in turfgrass management;* however, they are useful in preventing plant growth under fences and in other areas that are difficult to mow.

Herbicides may be applied to prevent weeds from infesting a turf or to control weeds already present. Bensulide is a *preemergence* herbicide applied in the springtime to prevent crabgrass. Once the weed has germinated, DSMA may be used as a postemergence treatment to selectively control the crabgrass invader.

Weed Control Groups

There are three groups of chemical controls for turf weeds: annual grasses, perennial grasses and other perennial monocots, and broadleaved weeds. The most common annual grasses found in home lawns are crabgrass, yellow foxtail, goosegrass, fall panicum, and barnyard grass. Common perennial grasses in turf include tall fescue, quackgrass, bentgrass, and nimblewill. Other perennial monocots include yellow nutsedge, wild garlic, and star of Bethlehem. Broadleaved weeds include annuals such as common chickweed or prostrate spurge and perennial weeds such as dandelions and white clover.

Perennial Grasses and Other Perennial Monocot Weeds

Perennial grassy weeds are considered to be the most difficult weed problems to deal with in lawns. Control options are limited because the weed species are biologically very similar to the lawn species. In fact, many perennial grassy weeds are not considered weeds per se but are considered desirable grasses when growing by themselves under a different set of conditions.

For example, several common perennial grasses are considered weeds when growing in Kentucky bluegrass lawns because they differ greatly in leaf width, color, or growth habit. Tall fescue is more coarse and grows in distinctive clumps when it occurs with Kentucky bluegrass. Creeping bentgrass, a very desirable turf species for golf courses, becomes a weed in bluegrass lawns because it appears as patches of finer grass, usually lighter in color. Zoysiagrass, a warm-season turf species, appears as patches of thick grass, dormant (straw-colored) for much of the spring and fall in Kentucky bluegrass or other cool-season grass lawns.

Additional perennial grasses and perennial monocot weeds are frequent weed problems. Quackgrass, a coarse species with thick underground stems (rhizomes), can be a major problem in lawns. Nimblewill, a creeping warm-season species, often appears as light-colored patches in lawns. Yellow nutsedge and wild garlic appear similar to grasses but belong to other plant families and are controlled with different herbicides.

One way to distinguish perennial grasses from annuals is the time of the year established plants are present. Perennials (other than nimblewill and zoysiagrass) appear as established green grasses early in spring, whereas most annual grasses, such as crabgrass, do not appear until late spring or early summer. Likewise, most annuals die off quickly in fall, but perennials do not.

Removing these weeds and weed patches by hand is one control option. It's important to get all of the plant, as many have underground or above-ground stems (rhizomes or stolons). These stems enable these species to spread quite readily; so, if broken or cut, they regrow.

Selective chemical control is not an option with most perennial grassy weed species. Unlike selective herbicides used on annual grasses (for example, crabgrass), nonselective herbicides used to control perennial weed grasses also may damage the lawn species. For this reason, spraying over the lawn is not suggested unless the problem is severe enough that all grasses must be killed and the lawn reestablished.

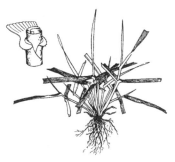

Tall Fescue

Quackgrass

Using a nonselective herbicide, such as glyphosate, you can spot treat patches of the undesirable species. After weeds and portions of lawn die, reseed with desirable grass species. Treating in early to mid-August is generally thought of as the best timing (late July to early August for nimblewill and zoysiagrass), as late August into early September is the most favorable time for reseeding. If you are resodding the area afterwards, there is a longer period of time to treat the weeds. Keep in mind, however, that the weed species must be actively growing to be controlled by glyphosate. Allow 10 to 14 days to determine if weeds have been completely controlled.

Other perennial monocot weeds require different chemical controls and are difficult to control. For these weeds, consult a lawn care professional or your local Extension office to discuss methods of chemical weed control.

Broadleaved Weeds

Broadleaved weeds, such as dandelion, clover, and creeping Charlie, are weed problems in turf because they have obvious differences in leaf shape, growth habit, and flower shape and color. Trying to determine why these weeds have invaded a lawn is the first step in managing broadleaved weeds in lawns. Weeds can be indicators of underlying problems. For example, ground ivy invades lawns in shade, while knotweed may indicate soil compaction. Assorted weeds may indicate overall poor conditions for lawn grasses and/or poor management.

After identifying the weeds present, step two for controlling broadleaved weeds should be to review lawn care practices and make adjustments as needed to ensure a good stand of grass. Sound lawn care practices should promote a healthy, vigorous turf able to prevent and compete with weed invasions. These practices include proper selection and establishment, fertilization, watering, mowing, thatch management, and related practices. Alter the environment that may be favoring weeds, such as reducing shade or improving poor soil conditions.

The third step is removal of existing broadleaved weeds. Pulling by hand is one option; be sure to get as much of the root system as possible.

Chemical control of these weeds is most often accomplished using postemergence herbicides. These herbicides are systemic, that is, the herbicides are absorbed by plant organs and translocated throughout the weed. Postemergence broadleaved herbicides found in garden centers typically include 2,4-D (2,4-dichlorophenoxyacetic acid); mecoprop or MCPP (2-(2-methyl-4-chlorophenoxy) propionic acid); or dicamba (3,6-dichloro-o-anisic acid); with two- and three-way combinations available (Table 3). Additional herbicides are available to commercial landscape care services for use on lawns.

When using any chemical pest control, be sure to read, understand, and follow the label directions for proper use of these chemicals. If mishandled or misapplied, postemergence broadleaved herbicides may damage or kill many desirable ornamental or edible plants in the landscape.

There are general guidelines for using broadleaved herbicides on lawns. Avoid windy days, as these materials can damage many landscape and garden plants if they drift (spray droplets land off the lawn). Also avoid hot days (over 85°F) and periods when weeds are heat- or drought-stressed. It's best to have adequate soil moisture, but no rain for 24 hours after application. Do not mow turf for a few days before and after application. Consider spot-treating weeds rather than broadcasting weed killer over the entire area. Use caution on newly seeded areas; wait four mowings before treating a newly seeded lawn, and wait 30 days before seeding an area treated with broadleaved herbicides. Refer to the label for potential hazards when used on lawns over the root zone of trees (such as with dicamba).

Creeping Charlie

Buckhorn Plantain

Dandelion

Table 3. Postemergence Herbicide Control of Broadleaved Weeds in Turf

Weeds controlled	2,4-D	MCPP	dicamba	Combination of all three materials
Black medic	..	xo	x	x
Broadleaved plantain	x	..	..	x
Buckhorn plantain	x	..	..	x
Common chickweed	..	xx	x	x
Curly dock	xo	..	x	x
Dandelion	x	xx	x	x
Ground ivy (creeping Charlie)	..	xo	xx	x
Henbit	xo	xo	x	x
Knotweed	..	xo	x	x
Postrate spurge	..	xo	xx	x
Thistles	xx	xo	x	x
Violets[a]	..	..	..	..
White clover	xo	x	x	x
Wild onion	xo	..	xx	x
Yarrow	xo	..	x	x
Yellow woodsorrel	xo	xo	xo	x

NOTE: All herbicides listed should be applied when weeds are actively growing. Turfgrass species exhibit different tolerances to these herbicides. Follow label directions for appropriate turfgrass species, rates, timing, and degree of safety when used near trees and shrubs.

.. Lack of a rating for herbicide–weed combinations indicates that information was unavailable at time of publication.

x Usually provides adequate weed control.

xx Multiple applications may be necessary for control.

xo May provide only partial weed control.

[a]Violets are best controlled using broadleaved herbicides containing triclopyr. Products containing triclopyr can be applied by professional turf specialists.

Early fall to midfall can be a good time to control cool-season annual weeds, such as henbit, and cool-season perennial broadleaved weeds, such as dandelions. Control is often good as weeds prepare for winter dormancy. Moreover, as weeds die following the herbicide application, lawns spread readily into bare areas in the cooler weather of fall. Spring and early summer applications may not provide control as good as occurs in autumn. In addition, warmer temperatures increase the chance of lawn injury. Regardless of the time of year, best control is achieved when weeds are young and actively growing.

Annual Grasses

In home lawns, crabgrass and other annual grassy weeds are common problems that can be treated through both chemical and nonchemical methods. Proper lawn care practices to encourage a dense stand of vigorous grass are the best way to prevent weeds from invading. For example, mowing height can have a big impact; lawns mowed higher (over 2 inches) tend to have fewer problems with annual grasses such as crabgrass. Close-mowed lawns tend to open up, allowing weeds like crabgrass to invade. Light, frequent watering also favors crabgrass. Crabgrass often invades areas seeded in late spring because bare soil, frequent watering, and the onset of hot weather are ideal for its growth.

Crabgrass

In some situations, turf is grown in environments that favor weed growth and development. Many annual grassy weeds are more tolerant of wet or compacted soils or shade than are turfgrasses. Altering the growing environment to favor the turfgrass can shift the competitive edge away from weeds.

Herbicides (weed killers) are also available to manage annual weeds. Preemergence herbicides prevent annual grassy weeds such as crabgrass from emerging. Timing of application is very important, as the weed killer should be applied before the crabgrass emerges from the soil. Crabgrass germinates when soil temperatures are greater than 55 to 60°F for 5 to 10 consecutive days, and it can continue to germinate until soils reach 95°F. Other annual grasses germinate as soils get warmer than 60°F.

For central Illinois, mid- to late April is the suggested time for applying a preemergence crabgrass herbicide. In the southern portion of Illinois, make the application 1 to 2 weeks earlier, 1 to 2 weeks later in northern Illinois. If the spring is very warm, use the earlier dates; in cold, "late" springs, these materials could be applied during the later timing. Using forsythia's blooming as a guide is not dependable. Many preemergence crabgrass herbicides are available in combination with lawn fertilizer at garden supply stores, so the crabgrass prevention and spring fertilization can be done at the same time.

Some herbicides may be reapplied for extended control; refer to the label for timing and rates. Core-aerifying or dethatching should be done based on label instructions. One of the management problems associated with preemergence herbicides is seeding or overseeding practices. Except for the herbicide siduron (Tupersan), preemergence annual grass weed killers also damage germinating desirable grass seed. Siduron is often combined with starter fertilizer.

If crabgrass plants are appearing in lawns in mid- to late summer, remember that they are annual plants and die as temperatures drop in the fall. Postemergence crabgrass herbicides should be applied when crabgrass plants are very small; typically crabgrass is noticed too late for these to be effective. The suggested strategy to avoid crabgrass next season is to improve the lawn through cultural practices and consider a preemergence herbicide in the spring.

Preemergence Control

Authors

T. Voigt
Department of Natural Resources and Environmental Sciences
B. Spangenberg
Extension Educator, Horticulture

CHAPTER THREE

Controlling Weeds in the Home Garden

A weed is a plant growing where it is not wanted. Weeds compete with desirable plants for water, soil nutrients, sunlight, and gaseous components of the air needed for growth. Many weeds also harbor diseases and insects that may attack plants around the home.

Three general methods of weed control can be used in the home garden: (1) cultivation and mechanical removal (hoeing, pulling); (2) mulching (smothering of weeds); and (3) herbicides (weed killers). Usually, one or more of these methods is used.

Cultivation and Mechanical Removal

The combination of cultivation and mechanical removal is the safest and most common method for controlling weeds in small home gardens. Because only those weeds that are present can be controlled, the process must be repeated several times throughout the growing season. Adequate control of weeds with this method may be difficult during vacations or busy work periods.

Shave off deeply rooted weeds with a sharp hoe while gently breaking up the soil crust. Deep tillage can cause severe injury to shallow-rooted plants and can bring deeply buried weed seeds to the surface, where they can germinate. Keeping equipment sharp and in good condition helps to reduce injury to desirable plants. Hoe carefully around your plants, and hand-pull weeds close to the plants.

Weeds in small areas can be controlled by wheel hoes or hand hoes; in large gardens, use power equipment such as Rototillers and garden tractors. This equipment should be set shallow when used in a garden for weed control. To prevent root injury, avoid cultivating too close to crop plants.

Cultivating by Hoe

Mulching

Mulching controls weeds by preventing light from reaching the weed seeds or seedlings. This method controls many annual weeds—those that germinate from

Pulling Weeds by Hand

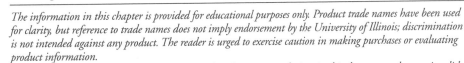

The information in this chapter is provided for educational purposes only. Product trade names have been used for clarity, but reference to trade names does not imply endorsement by the University of Illinois; discrimination is not intended against any product. The reader is urged to exercise caution in making purchases or evaluating product information.

Label registrations can change at any time. Thus the recommendations in this chapter may become invalid. The user must read carefully the entire, most recent label and follow all directions and restrictions. Purchase only enough pesticide for the current growing season.

seed each year. Perennial weeds (those that sprout each year from underground plant parts) usually must be removed by cultivation or hoeing.

The advantages of mulching include moisture conservation, prevention of soil crusting, reduction of erosion, increased soil temperatures in spring, and the ability to keep edible above-ground plant portions clean.

Organic Mulches

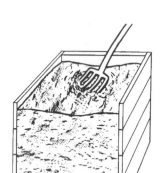

Compost Bin

The organic materials used most frequently for mulching include plant residues such as straw or hay (free of weed seeds); crushed corncobs; various nut hulls; leaf and grass composts; peat; wood products such as sawdust, wood chips, shredded bark, and shavings; and well-rotted animal manures. Use the most economical mulch available. A combination of several thicknesses of newspaper (use papers with black ink, not colored ink) covered by organic materials has shown promise as a summer mulch. For good results, apply these materials to a depth of 4 to 6 inches.

Applying natural mulch materials may require considerable hand labor. Most organic materials are bulky and must be hauled to the place of use, but this problem is not serious in small gardens.

Organic mulch materials	Nitrogen required for decomposition (pounds per ton of mulch)
Cocoa pods	6.0
Corncobs (ground)	22.5
Hay, grass clippings	7.6
Peanut hulls	8.5
Sawdust (fresh)	26.0
Wheat straw	17.6

As organic mulches decompose, they return organic matter and some plant nutrients to the soil and improve soil tilth. Added benefits are the prevention of soil compaction, conservation of soil moisture, erosion control on slopes, cooler soil temperatures in summer, and added attractiveness of the garden.

When organic materials are used, you may need to add nitrogen fertilizer to prevent nitrogen deficiency in the mulched crop. With alfalfa, clover, or other legume mulches, however, excess nitrogen is released during decomposition.

Synthetic Mulches

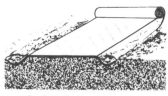

Black Polypropylene Cover

Common synthetic mulches include polyethylene, paper, paper-polyethylene combinations, black polypropylene mats, fiberglass mats, wax-coated papers, and aluminum and steel foils.

Polyethylene film is used in a thickness of 1 to 1½ mils (1 mil = 0.001 inch) and a width of 3 to 6 feet. Black polyethylene is preferable for the home vegetable garden because it prevents light from reaching the weed seedlings. It is generally not practical to use transparent polyethylene as a full-season mulch because weeds develop under the polyethylene.

To install the mulch, press the edges down into furrows and cover them firmly with soil. A push-type, one-wheel cultivator works well to open and close furrows. The mulch may also be installed by using a rake or shovel to cover the edges with soil. Do not throw excess soil on top of the mulch.

It is better to apply synthetic mulches in crop rows than to attempt covering the entire area. The area between the rows of polyethylene mulch must be carefully cultivated or hoed.

Use of polyethylene mulch increases soil temperatures in the spring and hastens the development of some crops.

Herbicides

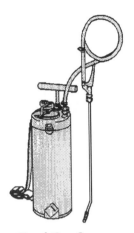

Hand Can Sprayer

Using herbicides in small ornamental and vegetable gardens containing several crop species is not a good practice because different flowers, vegetables, and weeds vary in their tolerance to herbicides. Some herbicides may remain in the soil longer than one growing season and may kill or injure some species the following year (especially if excessive rates are used). Ideally, a specific herbicide should be used for each crop species; but most people have small areas of several species in their gardens, making it impractical and expensive to buy the several herbicides that would be needed.

Application must be controlled carefully when a herbicide is used on small areas. The tendency is to apply additional amounts if the quantity measured out "looks" as if it is not enough. A low-percentage granular formulation is suggested for small garden areas. *CAUTION: Check the container label very carefully for rates of material to use and application techniques. Applications must be accurate and uniform. Excessive amounts may cause injury to the current or subsequent crops.*

If a gardener prefers not to remove weeds by hand in the home garden, **Dacthal** or **Treflan** may be used on several species. These herbicides may not be the most effective for a large planting of the individual fruit or vegetable species. Herbicides for these large plantings are listed in "Weed Control for Commercial Vegetable Crops" in the *Illinois Agricultural Pest Management Handbook* (revised annually).

Herbicides may be sold under several trade names. If you cannot identify the trade names on the container, look on the label for the common name or the chemical name of the active ingredients. The trade names listed in this publication are for products commonly used in Illinois. Products of identical content that are marketed under other trade names may be equally effective.

Trade name and common name	Chemical name
Dacthal (DCPA)	dimethyl 2,3,5,6-tetrachloroterephthalate
Roundup, Kleenup (glyphosate)	*N*-(phosphonomethyl)glycine
Treflan, Preen (trifluralin)	α,α,α-trifluoro-2,6-dinitro-*N-N*-dipropyl-p-toluidine
Devrinol (napropamide)	*N,N*-diethyl-2-(1-napthalenyloxy)-proprionamide

DCPA (Dacthal)

DCPA is a preemergence herbicide that controls very small weed seedlings soon after the weed seeds germinate. It does not control weeds that have emerged prior to application. The herbicide is most effective if rainfall occurs or the soil is irrigated within 2 to 3 days after application of the herbicide. Weeds that have already emerged should be removed before DCPA is applied.

DCPA is the best *multipurpose* herbicide for home-garden use. It is available as a 75 percent wettable-powder and as a 5 percent granular formulation. DCPA may be used for annual grass control in lawns; on a number of species of flowers; and on strawberries, broccoli, brussels sprouts, cauliflower, cabbage, dry and snap beans, cucumbers, squash, melons, collards, kale, mustard greens, turnips, garlic, onions, potatoes, sweet potatoes, yams, tomatoes, eggplants, peppers, and horseradish.

Do not use DCPA on beets, bugle weed, button pink, carnation, geum, germander, mesembryanthemum, pansy, phlox, sweet william, and telanthera.

A one-time application to all species is not always possible in a garden of flowers or vegetables because some plants in early growth stages are susceptible to injury. It is preferable to use DCPA at seeding or transplanting time if the species is adapted for it. When application must be delayed, remove emerged weeds, and then apply DCPA to prevent further weed development. Consult the container label for the appropriate application time.

DCPA is effective in controlling annual grasses that are a problem in the spring. Broadleaf weeds must be removed mechanically. Due to labeling changes, DCPA may become difficult to locate and purchase.

Yellow Foxtail

Trifluralin (Treflan, Preen)

Because trifluralin is used in soybean production in Illinois, it is widely available. It can be purchased as a liquid with 4 pounds of active ingredient per gallon for large areas or as a low-percentage granular form for smaller areas.

Trifluralin may be used for weed control in green, lima, and dry beans; broccoli; brussels sprouts; cabbage; cauliflower; carrots; kale; mustard greens; okra; peas; peppers; tomatoes; turnip greens; apricots; cherries; grapes; peaches; and plums. Established trees, some ornamentals, and many established flowers tolerate trifluralin. Do not use trifluralin on ground covers, sweet corn, strawberries, bramble fruits, or blueberries because injury may result.

Trifluralin must be moved into the soil soon after application to prevent loss of the chemical from the soil surface. A Rototiller or similar equipment should be used to mix trifluralin with the soil to a depth of 3 to 4 inches. When it is impractical to mix trifluralin with the soil mechanically, all emerged weeds should be removed and the herbicide incorporated into the soil by rainfall or sprinkle irrigation.

Large Crabgrass

The correct amount of trifluralin to use depends on the soil type. The appropriate amounts are shown on the container label.

Trifluralin is quite effective on annual grasses, but many broadleaved weeds must be removed mechanically.

Napropamide (Devrinol)

Napropamide is a preemergence herbicide. It should be incorporated into the soil by mechanical means or irrigation. Control existing weeds before applying napropamide.

Napropamide may be used in asparagus, tomatoes, peppers, strawberries, tree fruits, nuts, shrubs, and shade trees. It controls annual grasses such as barnyardgrass, crabgrass, fall panicum, and goosegrass. Broadleaf weeds that can be controlled by napropamide include carpetweed, purslane, lambsquarters, and pigweed.

Perennial Weed Control

Cultivation and mulching do not control most perennial weeds. Perennials can be controlled by removing the top growth to deplete the food (carbohydrate) supply in the underground storage tissues. This method may suppress the growth of perennial weeds, but completely eradicating the weeds with this method requires frequent recutting of the top growth.

Glyphosate (**Roundup, Kleenup**) must be applied to the foliage of green, actively growing plants to be effective. Because glyphosate has no soil activity, it may be applied in the early spring. It may also be applied in the fall, after the edible plants have been removed from the garden but while the perennial weeds are still growing. Because glyphosate is nonselective, do not apply it to (or let it drift onto) desirable or edible plants. Be sure to read the label for complete application instructions.

Glyphosate may be used to control perennial weeds in vegetable gardens where labeled vegetable species are to be grown. It must not be applied where nonlabeled vegetable species are to be grown. If gardeners in areas that are infested with perennial weeds are willing to restrict their choice of crops for one year, this method can effectively reduce the weeds. To find out which species are labeled, check the glyphosate label or contact your local Extension office.

Pigweed

Pesticide Safety

Phenoxy and Dicamba

Phenoxy herbicides (**2,4-D and others**) and dicamba (**Banvel**) are used to control broadleaf weeds in corn, turf areas, and roadways. Most flowers, shrubs, shade trees, small fruits, tree fruits, and vegetables are susceptible to injury by these herbicides. When applying these materials, be sure that direct spray, drifting spray, or fumes do not reach susceptible plants.

Use the amine formulation of 2,4-D, which is less volatile and does not drift as easily as the esters; and apply it under calm conditions and temperatures below 80 to 85°F. A sprayer used to apply phenoxy herbicides or dicamba on grass should not be used to apply other pesticides on gardens. Phenoxys usually cannot be cleaned out of sprayers thoroughly enough to avoid injury to broadleaved plants.

Soil Deactivation

If a garden area becomes contaminated with a persistent herbicide or a soil sterilant, this area can be decontaminated by applying activated carbon to inactivate the herbicide. See *Horticulture Fact Sheet VC-15-81*, "Testing for and Deactivating Herbicide Residues," available from Horticulture Facts, University of Illinois, 1105 Plant Sciences Laboratory, 1201 S. Dorner Drive, Urbana, IL 61801, (217)333-0350. The first copy is free, additional copies 25 cents each.

Disposal of Pesticide Containers and Surplus Pesticides

Use pesticides safely. Read the labels. If pesticides are handled or applied improperly, or if unused containers are disposed of improperly, injury can occur to humans, domestic animals, desirable plants, pollinating insects, and fish or other wildlife. Water supplies also can become contaminated. Use pesticides only when needed, and handle them with care. Follow directions, and heed all precautions on container labels.

Store all pesticides in a cool, dry, locked storage area so that they are not accessible to children, unknowledgeable persons, or animals. Do not dispose of pesticides through sewage systems or where they can run off into drainage ditches or bodies of water. Haul them or have them hauled to a sanitary landfill for burial.

Never place aerosol cans on a stove or heater or near any source of heat that might exceed 120°F. Store in a cool place—not in the hot sun. Have empty aerosol cans hauled away and buried by experienced disposal crews. Do not incinerate aerosol cans.

Classification of Herbicides

The U.S. Environmental Protection Agency classifies herbicides for *general use* or *restricted use.* An Illinois resident wishing to use a herbicide classified for restricted use must be certified as a private or commercial pesticide applicator by the Illinois Department of Agriculture. Your local Extension office can give you details on this program. No herbicide discussed in this article has been classified for restricted use.

Author

D. Williams
*Department of Natural Resources
and Environmental Sciences*

CHAPTER FOUR

Managing Diseases in the Home Vegetable Garden

I *Rapum maius.*
Great Turneps.

Diseases of vegetables grown in the home garden may reduce both the yield and the quality of vegetables. Controlling such diseases often determines success or failure and adds immeasurably to the pleasure derived from a garden.

Diseases of vegetables are caused by microorganisms, including fungi, bacteria (including mycoplasmas and spiroplasmas), viruses, and nematodes. These organisms are spread by wind-blown or water-splashed spores, by insects, by infected seeds and transplants, by the movement of infested soil, and by humans handling wet plants.

Many vegetable diseases can be controlled using an integrated disease-control program. Such a program involves the use of

◆ crop rotation

◆ sanitation

◆ disease-resistant or -tolerant varieties

◆ disease-free seeds or transplants

◆ sound horticultural practices

◆ balanced soil fertility (based on soil tests)

◆ proper and timely applications of pesticides.

No single pest-management practice can control all diseases of any vegetable crop. Therefore, several measures must be used to achieve satisfactory control.

Disease Control Before Planting

Choose and Prepare the Site

The site for the vegetable garden should be well drained and have adequate sunlight (8 to 10 hours of direct sunshine per day) and good air circulation. The soil should have adequate soil fertility and the proper pH (5.5 to 7.0).

The information in this chapter is provided for educational purposes only. Product trade names have been used for clarity, but reference to trade names does not imply endorsement by the University of Illinois; discrimination is not intended against any product. The reader is urged to exercise caution in making purchases or evaluating product information.

Label registrations can change at any time. Thus the recommendations in this chapter may become invalid. The user must read carefully the entire, most recent label and follow all directions and restrictions. Purchase only enough pesticide for the current growing season.

If garden vegetables have been produced for several years in an area, sanitation and rotation practices can reduce the risk of disease-causing organisms that survive from preceding crops. It is important for disease-control purposes to remove or turn under dead and diseased plant material in the fall. Crop residues from healthy plants can be composted and returned to the garden.

Disease-causing fungi and bacteria can survive composting unless the decomposition of the crop residue is *complete,* a situation that seldom occurs. Therefore, we suggest that no diseased plant parts be placed in the compost pile. Some disease organisms even survive complete composting, including corn smut; clubroot of cabbage, broccoli, cauliflower, and other crucifers; Verticillium wilt of potato, tomato, pepper, and eggplant; and root-knot nematodes.

Turning under (plowing or tilling) crop residues in the fall helps prevent the overwintering of many disease-causing organisms. Besides destroying the "winter home" of various organisms, this practice also helps control the insects that transmit certain diseases. Also, crop debris that is turned under improves soil tilth and makes spring garden work easier.

Rotate Crops

Crop rotation is an important control measure because many disease-causing organisms attack only related plants in the same family. Unrelated plants do not serve as hosts on which these organisms can multiply. Therefore, if possible, avoid planting any vegetables *within* each of the following groups in the same location more than once every 3 or 4 years.

Cabbage

◆ **Cole crops** (cabbage family)—broccoli, brussels sprout, cabbage, cauliflower, chinese cabbage, kohlrabi, mustard greens, radish, rutabaga, and turnip.

◆ **Cucurbits** (cucumber family)—cucumber, gourd, muskmelon, pumpkin, squash (all types), and watermelon.

◆ **Solanaceous crops** (tomato family)—eggplant, husk tomato (ground cherry), pepper, potato, and tomato.

◆ **Chenopodiaceous crops**—beet (red and sugar) and spinach.

◆ **Amaryllidaceae** (onion family)—chives, garlic, leek, onion, and shallot.

◆ **Legumes**—beans (all types) and peas.

◆ **Umbelliferous crops**—carrots, celery, and parsnip.

Squash

For example, broccoli, cabbage, radish, or turnip should not be planted in the same location for two successive years. Cabbage could be followed with beans, a vine crop such as cucumber, or sweet corn.

Diseases affecting beans, peas, sweet corn, carrot, lettuce, spinach, rhubarb, okra, edible soybeans, and similar plants are usually specific to only one of these crops and generally do not infect others or members of the major vegetable crop groups.

Choose Disease-Resistant Varieties

The use of well-adapted, disease-resistant varieties is the simplest and most efficient method of controlling many diseases. Information on disease resistance is given in the following paragraphs. Listings of disease-resistant or -tolerant reactions for selected vegetable varieties, unless otherwise indicated, are based on the disease reactions reported by the various seed companies and have not necessarily been verified by independent research at the University of Illinois. Furthermore, a designation of resistance or tolerance does not necessarily mean that the plant is immune to the disease and shows no disease symptoms. Some varieties are partially resistant, and the expression of symptoms and development of the disease are reduced when compared to a susceptible variety. (See Tables 1 to 8.) Also, some forms of resistance are effective against only certain strains or races of the disease-causing agent. Thus, a variety described as being resistant to a particular disease can acquire that disease under certain circumstances.

Start with Disease-Free Seeds, Plants, and Planting Materials

Use Disease-free Seed

It is important to start with disease-free seeds or planting materials (bulbs, tubers, transplants, sets, etc.) to keep from introducing serious diseases into the garden. In general, gardeners are encouraged *not* to save their own seed but to purchase seed from reputable seed dealers. Hot-water soaks and fungicide seed treatments may be used to control the seedborne disease organisms that cause damping-off and seed rots. Because temperature controls and timing must be precise, home gardeners usually buy seed that has already been treated with hot water by the seed producer. Hot-water treatment of cabbage, broccoli, brussels sprout, and cauliflower seed is particularly important. More information on hot-water and fungicide seed treatments may be found in *Report on Plant Disease*, no. 915, "Vegetable Seed Treatment," available from the Department of Crop Sciences, N533 Turner Hall, 1102 S. Goodwin Ave., Urbana, IL 61801.

Many vegetable seeds are coated with a fungicide, as evidenced by the colored coating on the seed. Untreated seed can be treated by the home gardener by placing a small quantity (the size of one or two matchheads) of captan or thiram in the seed packet and shaking the packet for a minute or two to cover the seed thoroughly. Excess protectant may be sifted out before planting the seed.

Do not plant diseased material (for example, transplants, sets, bulbs, or tubers). All planting material should be healthy and free of yellowing and brown or black spots, and it should not be stunted or show poor development. Only certified, disease-free potato tubers or sweet potato slips should be used. Examine transplants thoroughly for signs of leaf or stem disease. It never pays to buy and plant diseased transplants, no matter what the price!

Damping-off diseases affecting home-grown vegetable transplants can be controlled by the use of disease-free soil and fungicides. Specific recommendations are given in *Report on Plant Disease*, no. 916, "Damping-off Diseases of Vegetables," available from the Department of Crop Sciences, N533 Turner Hall, 1102 S. Goodwin Ave., Urbana, IL 61801.

Cultural Practices

Cultural practices—such as controlling weeds, planting at the right time, planting at the proper depth and spacing, employing cages or stakes, and watering when the temperature is rising to promote a rapid drying of the foliage—can help control many foliar diseases. Mulches help to control fruit rots and aid in control of blossom-end rot of tomato, pepper, and vine crops by maintaining a uniform supply of moisture in the soil. Weed control in and around the garden reduces the risk of attacks by viruses that overwinter in these plants. Do not work or harvest wet plants because this can spread many diseases, particularly those caused by bacterial and fungal pathogens.

Disease Control During the Growing Season

Many diseases, such as the early blight disease of potato and tomato, occur each year despite all preplanting precautions. For such diseases, applications of fungicides and bactericides to the growing plants may be needed. The best way to apply these materials is as sprays *before* the disease occurs. Often a wetting agent such as liquid detergent or soap (½ tsp in 1 gal of the fungicide solution) is added to obtain a more thorough wetting and coverage of the foliage. Apply sprays to the point of runoff, on a 7- to 10-day schedule. This schedule maintains a fresh or effective covering of fungicide and protects the new growth. Fungicides and bactericides currently recommended for use on vegetables are listed in Table 9.

Principal Diseases of Vegetables and Recommended Control Measures

Asparagus

Rust

Grow resistant varieties (Mary Washington, Martha Washington, Viking, Waltham Washington, or hybrids, including Jersey Centennial, Jersey Giant, and Greenwich). Start spray applications after harvest, and continue until mid-August on a 10-day schedule with an approved fungicide.

Crown and root rots

Maintain proper fertility and good soil drainage. Avoid overcutting. The hybrid varieties listed above have some resistance to Fusarium crown and root rot.

Beans

Seed decay and damping-off

Use captan- or thiram-treated seed. Plant in a warm, moist, well-prepared seedbed.

Bacterial blights

Practice a 2- to 3-year crop rotation. Do not save seed from infected plants. Purchase seed from a reputable seed dealer. Spray a copper-based bactericide such as Kocide or copper sulfate at the first sign of disease, and continue on a 7-day schedule until harvest. *Do not* work among wet plants.

Rust

Grow rust-resistant varieties. Apply fungicides at the first sign of disease, and continue on a 7-day schedule.

Mosaics

Grow resistant varieties. Table 1 contains a list of disease-resistant bean varieties.

White mold

Avoid wet locations with a history of white mold. Apply an approved fungicide when 10 to 25% of the blossoms are open and again at full bloom.

Beets

Seed decay and damping-off

Plant seed treated with thiram or captan.

Leaf spots

Practice a 2- to 3-year crop rotation. Spray with an approved fungicide on a 7-day schedule.

Table 1. Disease-Resistant Bean Varieties

		Disease		
Variety	Seed sources[a]	Common bean mosaic	New York 15 strain of bean mosaic	Rust
Green snap beans				
Bush Blue Lake 274	BP, GU, HM, RU, SS, SW	x	x	
Contender	GU, RU, SS, ST	x		
Provider	HM, RU, SS, ST	x	x	
Tendercrop	BP, GU, HM, RU, ST, SW	x	x	
Topcrop	BP, GU, RU, SS	x		
Pole snap beans				
Blue Lake Pole	BP, GU, SS, ST	x		
Dade	SS	x		x
Kentucky Wonder Rust Resistant	BP, FM, GU, SW			x
Yellow wax beans				
Cherokee	GU, RU, SS	x	x	
Goldcrop	BP, SS, ST, SW	x	x	
Sungold	HM, SS	x	x	

[a]For a key to seed sources, see page 72.

Carrots

Seed rot and damping-off

Plant seed treated with captan or thiram.

Leaf spots

Practice a 2- or 3-year crop rotation. Spray weekly with an approved fungicide, starting about mid-June. Varieties resistant to Cercospora leaf spot include Gold Pak, Spartan Fancy, and Danvers 126.

Destroy infected plants as soon as they appear. Apply insecticide sprays for leafhopper control. Spray before removing infected plants.

Cole Crops (cabbage, broccoli, brussels sprout, cauliflower, chinese cabbage, kohlrabi, mustard greens, radish, rutabaga, and turnip)

Seed decay, damping-off, black rot, and blackleg

Plant hot water–treated seed that also has been treated with captan or thiram. Several black rot–resistant cabbage varieties are now available. See Table 2.

Leaf spots and blights

Practice a 2- or 3-year crop rotation for broccoli, cabbage, cauliflower, and brussels sprout. Apply an approved fungicide on a 7-day schedule.

Clubroot

Purchase disease-free transplants. PCNB (Terraclor) may be added to the transplant water.

Fusarium yellows

Grow only varieties that are resistant to yellows. Table 2 contains a list of cabbage varieties that are disease resistant.

Table 2. Disease-Resistant Cabbage Varieties

Variety	Seed sources[a]	Disease	
		Yellows	Black rot
Bravo	HM, RU	x	x
Conquest	AS	x	
Golden Acre	RU, SS	x	
Gosmet	FM, ST	x	
Green Cap	AS, RU	x	x
Market Prize	HM, RU	x	
Olympic	RS	x	x
Savoy Ace	HM, RU	x	
Solid Blue #770	AC	x	x
Stonehead	BP, RU, ST	x	

[a]For a key to seed sources, see page 72.

Cucurbits (cucumber, gourds, muskmelon, pumpkin, squash, and watermelon)

Seed rot and damping-off	Plant seed treated with captan. Plant in a warm, well-prepared seedbed.
Angular leafspot	Practice a 2- to 3-year crop rotation. Spray with a fixed-copper bactericide, such as Kocide 101 or copper sulfate. Remove diseased plant material. Plant resistant varieties whenever possible.
Anthracnose, Alternaria leaf blight, downy mildew, blossom blights, fruit rots and spots, and gummy stem blight or black rot	Practice a 2- to 3-year crop rotation. Apply an approved fungicide at weekly intervals, starting when the plants are in the two-leaf stage. Adequate nitrogen fertility is essential for the successful control of Alternaria leaf blight. Plant resistant varieties when available.
Bacterial wilt	Spray with an insecticide to control cucumber beetles as soon as the seedlings "crack" the soil but before they emerge. Continue weekly spraying until the plants are in bloom. Spray in the evening to avoid killing bees.
Fusarium wilt	Grow only cantaloupe and watermelon varieties that are resistant to Fusarium wilt. Table 3 lists disease-resistant muskmelon (cantaloupe) varieties, and Table 4 lists disease-resistant watermelon varieties.
Powdery mildew	Spray with an approved fungicide at the first sign of disease, and continue to spray weekly thereafter. Grow resistant varieties.
Mosaic and other viral diseases	Grow resistant varieties where possible. Only cucumbers resistant to cucumber mosaic should be grown. Table 5 lists disease-resistant cucumber varieties.

Table 3. Disease-Resistant Muskmelon (Cantaloupe) Varieties

		Disease		
Variety	Seed sources[a]	Fusarium wilt	Downy mildew	Powdery mildew
Ambrosia	AC, BP, RU		x	x
Harper	ST	x		
Palsau	AC, RU, ST, SW	x		x
Saticoy	AC, RU, SW	x		x
Starship	HM, RU	x		x

[a]For a key to seed sources, see page 72.

Table 4. Disease-Resistant Watermelon Varieties

		Disease	
Variety	Seed sources[a]	Fusarium	Anthracnose
Allsweet	AC, RS, RU, SS	x	x
Charleston Gray	AC, AS, BP, GU, RS, RU, SS	x	x
Congo	GU, RS, RU		x
Crimson Sweet	AC, AS, BP, GU, HM, RS, RU, SS, ST, SW	x	x
Jubilee	AC, AS, HM, RS, RU, SS	x	x

[a]For a key to seed sources, see page 72.

Table 5. Disease-Resistant Cucumber Varieties

		Disease[b]					
Variety	Seed sources[a]	CMV	Scab	DM	PM	AN	AL
Burpless no. 26	BP, RS, RU	x		x	x		
Dasher II	AC, RU, ST, SW	x	x	x	x	x	x
Marketmore 76	AS, GU, HM, RS, RU, SS, ST, SW	x	x	x	x		
Medalist	HM	x	x	x	x		
Poinsett 76	AC, AS, HM, RS, RU, SS		x	x	x	x	x
Sweet Slice	BP, RU, ST, SW	x	x	x	x	x	x

[a]For a key to seed sources, see page 72.
[b]CMV = cucumber mosaic virus; DM = downy mildew; PM = powdery mildew; AN = anthracnose; AL = Alternaria.

Eggplant

Seed rot, damping-off, and Phomopsis blight　　Plant seed treated with captan or thiram.

Phomopsis blight and other fruit rots　　Practice a 2- or 3-year crop rotation. Spray weekly with an approved fungicide when fruits are half size, or when disease first appears.

Verticillium wilt　　Mulching with plastic may help reduce losses.

Onion

Smut, seed rot, and damping-off　　Plant seed treated with thiram or captan.

Leaf diseases　　Practice a 2- or 3-year crop rotation. Spray weekly with an approved fungicide. Carefully follow label directions regarding the days between the last spray and harvest.

Bulb rots　　Control leaf diseases. Avoid storing improperly cured or injured bulbs. Let all onion tops fall over (ripen) naturally. Store under cool, dry conditions. Do not expose cured bulbs to sunscald, water, or high humidity.

Fusarium basal rot　　Grow resistant varieties. Alba Globe, Nugget, and Spartan Banner are resistant.

Peas

Seed rot and damping-off　　Plant seed treated with captan or thiram.

Root rot　　Plant early in well-drained soils. Use a fungicide seed treatment.

Fusarium wilt　　Plant only varieties that are resistant to wilt. See Table 6 for a list of disease-resistant varieties.

Table 6. Disease-Resistant Pea Varieties

Variety	Seed sources[a]	Disease[b]						
		FUS	BYMV	DM	PEV	CW	PM	PSV
Green Arrow	BP, GU, HM, RU, ST, SW	x		x				
Knight	AC, HM, RU, SS	x	x		x		x	
Lincoln	GU, RU, SS, ST	x						
Oregon Sugar Pod no. 2	AC, BP, HM, RU, SS, SW	x			x		x	x
Sugar Ann	AC, GU, RU					x		

[a]For a key to seed sources, see page 72.
[b]FUS = Fusarium; BYMV = beet yellow mosaic virus; DM = downy mildew; PEV = pea enation virus; CW = common wilt; PM = powdery mildew; PSV = pea streak virus.

Peppers

Seed rot and damping-off	Plant seed treated with captan or thiram.
Bacterial spot	Use the hot-water seed treatment; or dip seed in a solution of 1 part household bleach to 3 parts water, and rinse with water. Follow with a fungicide seed treatment. Apply weekly sprays of a fixed-copper fungicide, such as Kocide 101 or copper sulfate, through the bloom stage. Rotate to crops outside the tomato family.
Phytophthora blight	Avoid planting in low, water-logged areas. Plant on hills or raised beds. Plant resistant varieties. Do not overwater.
Tobacco mosaic	Plant resistant varieties. See Table 7 for a list of these varieties.

Table 7. Bell Pepper Varieties Resistant to One or More Viruses

Variety	Seed sources[a]	Disease	
		Tomato mosaic virus	Potato virus Y
Bell Boy F$_1$ Hybrid	RU, ST, SW	x	
Bell Captain	AC, RU, ST	x	
Bell Tower	AC, RS, RU, ST	x	x
California Wonder 300	AC, AS, BP, HM, RU, SS, ST	x	
Grande Rio 66	HM	x	
Keystone Resistant Giant	AS, HM, SS	x	
Lady Bell	HM	x	
Yolo Wonder	AS, FM, SS, ST	x	

[a]For a key to seed sources, see page 72.

Potato

Viruses, late blight, Verticillium wilt, and ring rot	Plant only "certified" disease-free seed.
Seed piece rots	Treat cut seed pieces with captan as a dust or dip. Plant in warm soil (over 50°F) after the cut surfaces have corked over (suberized).
Early blight and late blight	Practice a 2- or 3-year crop rotation. Destroy or remove cull tubers. Spray at weekly intervals, starting when the plants are 4 to 6 inches tall, with an approved fungicide. Plant varieties resistant to late blight.
Verticillium wilt and root-knot nematodes	Plant resistant varieties.
Scab	Plant resistant varieties, or adjust the soil pH to 5.2 to 5.5. Use fungicide seed-piece treatments. Good scab-resistant red potato varieties are Norland and Norchief. Good scab-resistant white potato varieties are Superior and Norgold Russet.

Potato (cont.)

Storage rots	Store only disease-free, unbruised tubers. Allow tubers to cure at 60°F for 5 to 7 days before reducing the temperature to 36 to 40°F (if possible).

Sweet Corn

Seed rot and damping-off	Plant seed treated with captan or thiram.
Smut	Plant resistant varieties. Remove smut galls from the garden before they break. Do not compost smutted corn or infected corn residues.
Stewart's bacterial wilt	Plant resistant varieties. (See Table 8 for a list of varieties resistant to this and other diseases.) Control flea beetles with a recommended insecticide. Early season control is particularly important.
Foliage blights and rust	Plant varieties resistant to northern and southern corn leaf blights and rusts. Apply an approved fungicide. However, the use of fungicides is rarely justified. Diseased plant material should be removed from the garden. Blighted leaf tissue is safe to compost.
Maize dwarf mosaic	Plant as far from johnsongrass as possible. Control wild johnsongrass plants. Plant tolerant varieties.

Table 8. Disease-Resistant Sweet Corn Varieties

Variety[a]	Color[b]	Seed sources[c]	Disease[d]					
			SW	CS	CR	NCLB	SCLB	MDM
Standard Sugary (SU)								
Comet	W	AS	x		x	x		
Gold Cup	Y	HM	x		x			
Honey 'n Frost	B	SW	x	x	x	x	x	
Jubilee	Y	RS, SW		x	x			
Seneca Horizon	Y	HM, RU, ST, SW			x			
Silver Chief	W	AS	x			x		
Silver Queen	W	AC, BP, GU, HM, RU, ST, SW	x			x		
Spring Dance	Y	ST				x		
Stylepak	Y	FM, ST	x					
Sugar Loaf	Y	SS	x		x	x		
Sundance	Y	HM, ST						x
Sweet Sue	B	HM	x					
Sugar Enhancer (SE)								
Calico Belle	B	AS	x		x			
Classic	Y	AS	x	x	x	x	x	
Esteem	Y	HM			x			x
Incredible	Y	HM, RU, SW	x	x	x			

[a]Disease reactions are based on evaluations at the University of Illinois and other universities.
[b]Colors: W = white; Y = yellow; B = bi-color.
[c]For a key to seed sources, see page 72.
[d]SW = Stewart's wilt; CS = common smut; CR = common rust; NCLB = northern corn leaf blight; SCLB = southern corn leaf blight; MDM = maize dwarf mosaic.

Table 8. Disease-Resistant Sweet Corn Varieties (cont.)

Variety[a]	Color[b]	Seed sources[c]	Disease[d]					
			SW	CS	CR	NCLB	SCLB	MDM
Sugar Enhancer (SE) (cont.)								
Miracle	Y	AC, BP, RU, ST	x	x	x	x		
Platinum Lady	W	BP, RU, ST		x	x			
Sugar Buns	Y	RU, ST, SW			x	x		
Tuxedo	Y	CR	x	x	x	x	x	
Super Sweet (SH2)								
Challenger	Y	AS	x			x		
Florida Staysweet	Y		x			x	x	
How Sweet It Is	W	AC, BP, GU, RU	x			x		
Phenomenal	B	RU, ST, SW		x		x	x	
Super Sweet 7710	Y	AC	x			x	x	
Supersweet Jubilee	Y	RS		x				
Sweet Belle	Y	AS	x	x		x		
Sweetie 82	Y	SW	x	x	x		x	

[a]Disease reactions are based on evaluations at the University of Illinois and other universities.
[b]Colors: W = white; Y = yellow; B = bi-color.
[c]For a key to seed sources, see page 72.
[d]SW = Stewart's wilt; CS = common smut; CR = common rust; NCLB = northern corn leaf blight; SCLB = southern corn leaf blight; MDM = maize dwarf mosaic.

Spinach

Seed rot and damping-off   Plant seed treated with captan or thiram.

Cucumber mosaic virus   Plant resistant varieties.

Downy mildew or blue mold   Plant resistant varieties.

The variety Melody has resistance to both cucumber mosaic virus and downy mildew.

Sweet Potato

Black rot, scurf, foot rot, wilt, and soil rot   Buy certified, disease-free slips. Plant resistant varieties. Use a 3- or 4-year rotation. The varieties Allgold and Centennial have good resistance to wilt and soil rot; Allgold also has resistance to black rot.

Storage diseases   Do not expose roots to temperatures below 55°F. Immediately after digging, cure the roots at 85°F and high humidity for 10 to 14 days. Store at 55°F. Never store in airtight bags or containers. Apply an approved fungicide as a postharvest dip. Follow the manufacturer's directions carefully.

Tomato

Seed rot, damping-off, bacterial spot, bacterial canker, and tobacco mosaic virus	Plant seed that has been treated with hot water or acid and then treated with captan or thiram. Purchase seed or transplants only from reputable dealers. Soaking seed in copper sulfate solution (2 oz per gal of water) or dipping it in bleach solution as described under the section on peppers helps prevent bacterial spot and canker if seeds are saved.
Bacterial spot	Plant certified, disease-free seed or transplants. Practice a 2- or 3-year crop rotation. Spray plants weekly with a fixed-copper fungicide, beginning with the first sign of disease, through the bloom stage.
Early blight, Septoria leaf blight, anthracnose, buckeye rot, and soil rots	Spray weekly with an approved fungicide. Practice a 2- or 3-year crop rotation. Remove or destroy infected plant parts. Carefully follow label directions regarding the days between the last spray and harvest. Staking or caging plants and providing good air circulation helps reduce foliar diseases. Staking, caging, or mulching also helps prevent fruit rots, such as anthracnose, buckeye rot, and soil rot. Varieties such as Floramerica, Jetstar, Manlucie, Roma VF, and Supersonic have some tolerance to the early blight disease.
Blossom-end rot	Maintain uniform soil moisture by mulching the plants and irrigating when needed. Avoid heavy pruning, excessive nitrogen applications, and damage to the roots by cultivation or hoeing.
Verticillium and Fusarium wilts	Grow only VF- or VFN-resistant varieties. Many varieties are available.
Root-knot nematodes	Grow VFN-resistant varieties.
Viruses	Avoid contact between potatoes and tomatoes to prevent "double infections" of potato and tomato viruses. Wash hands thoroughly with soap and hot water before handling your plants. Do not use tobacco when working with tomatoes.

Key to Seed Sources

AC	Abbott & Cobb, Inc.
AS	Asgrow Seed Co.
BP	Burpee-Market More Seed Co.
CR	Crookham Seed Co.
FM	Ferry-Morse Seed Co.
GU	Gurney's Seed & Nursery Co.
HM	Harris Moran Seed Co.
RS	Rogers Seeds
RU	Rupp Seeds, Inc.
SS	Sunseeds Genetics, Inc.
ST	Stokes Seeds Ltd., Inc.
SW	Seedway/Agway, Inc.

Table 9. Fungicides for Use by Vegetable Gardeners

Crop	benomyl[a]	chlorothalonil[b]	copper[c]	maneb	sulfur
Asparagus					
Rust			x		
Bean					
Anthracnose		x			
Bacterial blights			x		
Gray mold		x			
Rust		x			x
White mold	x				
Broccoli, cabbage, cauliflower					
Alternaria leaf spot		x	x	x	
Black rot			x		
Downy mildew		x	x	x	
Carrots					
Alternaria leaf spot		x			
Cercospora leaf spot		x	x		
White mold	x				
Cucumber, melons, pumpkin, squash					
Alternaria leaf spot		x		x	
Angular leaf spot			x		
Anthracnose	x	x		x	
Downy mildew		x	x	x	
Gummy stem blight	x	x		x	
Powdery mildew	x	x	x		x
Onion					
Botrytis blast		x		x	
Downy mildew		x	x	x	
Purple leaf blotch		x	x	x	
Pepper					
Anthracnose				x	
Bacterial spot			x		
Phytophthora blight				x	
Potato					
Early blight		x	x	x	
Late blight		x	x	x	

NOTE: Fungicides registered for control of specific diseases are indicated by an x. Label registrations can change at any time. Therefore, these recommendations may become invalid. The user must read carefully the entire, most recent label and follow all directions and restrictions.

[a]The fungicide benomyl is sold as Benlate.

[b]The fungicide chlorothalonil is sold as Bravo, Terranil, and several other names.

[c]There are many copper-based fungicides available, including bordeaux mixture, copper sulfate, copper hydroxide, and copper oxychloride sulfate, which are sold under a variety of trade names.

Table 9. Fungicides for Use by Vegetable Gardeners (cont.)

Crop	benomyl[a]	chlorothalonil[b]	copper[c]	maneb	sulfur
Sweet corn					
Northern leaf blight		x		x	
Rust		x		x	
Tomato					
Anthracnose		x	x	x	
Bacterial speck			x		
Bacterial spot			x		
Early blight		x	x	x	
Gray leaf spot	x	x		x	
Late blight		x	x	x	
Septoria leaf spot		x	x	x	
Sclerotinia stem rot	x				

NOTE: Fungicides registered for control of specific diseases are indicated by an x. Label registrations can change at any time. Therefore, these recommendations may become invalid. The user must read carefully the entire, most recent label and follow all directions and restrictions.
[a]The fungicide benomyl is sold as Benlate.
[b]The fungicide chlorothalonil is sold as Bravo, Terranil, and several other names.
[c]There are many copper-based fungicides available, including bordeaux mixture, copper sulfate, copper hydroxide, and copper oxychloride sulfate, which are sold under a variety of trade names.

Author

D. Eastburn
Department of Crop Sciences

CHAPTER FIVE

Managing Insect Pests in the Home, Yard, and Garden

2 *Aquileia rubra.*
Red Columbines.

Photo by Floyd Giles

Integrated Pest Management for Homeowners

Pest management should be conducted in as safe a manner as possible. Reducing the use of insecticides and other pesticides through integrated pest management (IPM) is a way to accomplish this goal. Two main components of IPM are (1) scouting for pests and (2) using a variety of methods to manage pest populations. These methods include prevention; use of resistant varieties; and use of mechanical, biological, cultural, and chemical tools.

Scouting

Scouting is the process of finding the suspected pest, identifying it, and determining if the pest is present in large enough numbers to justify management.

Finding the Suspected Pest

Indirect evidence may or may not indicate the presence of a pest. For instance:

◆ Holes in leaves may be caused by late frost damage, not by chewing insects.

◆ Sawdust piles in the home may be construction debris sifting through cracks or the consequence of mouse activity rather than the evidence of carpenter ants or other wood-destroying insects.

It is important to find the insects or other pests actually responsible for the damage observed. Do not assume the damage is pest-related.

Identification

Once found, the suspect pest must be identified. In some situations, an insect that is present in great numbers may not be the cause of damage. For instance:

◆ Lady beetle (larvae and adults) and other aphid-destroying insects are often found in large numbers in the midst of damage caused by aphids.

◆ Large numbers of ants in the lawn rarely damage the lawn and have little relationship to the number of ants that enter the home.

Identification is also important because some kinds of insects are more damaging than others. Once you know what kind of insect is present, you can better judge if the potential damage justifies management measures. Knowing the identity of a pest also helps you learn about the insect's biology, enabling you to use available IPM tools to manage the insect.

Colorado Potato Beetle

Pest Population Size

Knowing the number of pests present can help you estimate their impact and whether or not there is sufficient cause to spend time and money on management. Different numbers of pests may be damaging in different situations. For instance:

◆ One cockroach in a home is usually sufficient cause to start some kind of management measure, but a few in an outbuilding probably will not invade the home and would not require managing.

◆ A small number of white grubs in a vegetable garden may cause heavy damage to root crops such as potatoes, carrots, and onions but cause no yield loss to nonroot crops such as tomatoes, beans, and cabbage.

Pest Population Management Methods

Various management measures may be used on pest populations. Individual IPM tools may be more or less successful, depending on the situation and the biology of the pest. A good IPM program usually combines two or more of these tools to manage the pest.

Population Size

Prevention

Pest problems can be avoided by keeping an insect pest out of the area where the crop is being grown. This normally is accomplished through quarantines by governmental agencies, with the assistance and cooperation of the public.

◆ Efforts have been made to keep gypsy moths and pine shoot beetles out of Illinois, and to keep Africanized honey bees out of the United States. Reducing pest spread for even a few years can be worthwhile.

Another form of pest prevention is simply avoiding the food plants of particular pests. Careful selection of landscape or garden plants can prevent pest problems that might otherwise be difficult to manage. Planting resistant varieties and using some forms of cultural management may help prevent pest problems.

Resistant Varieties

Pest problems can be prevented or lessened by growing plant varieties or raising animals that are not heavily attacked by the pest in question.

◆ Birch varieties such as Whitespire or Heritage river birch are less susceptible to bronze birch borer than is the common paper birch.

◆ Butternut squash is less susceptible to squash vine borer than is acorn or blue hubbard squash. Zucchini squash appears to be the most susceptible summer squash variety.

Cultural Management

Pests are managed by changing the methods used to grow or maintain the plants, animals, or buildings that are attacked.

Birch Branch

◆ *Planting time:* Early plantings of sweet corn have reduced levels of damage by corn earworm. Planting zucchini squash early allows more of the crop to be harvested before damage by squash vine borer occurs.

◆ *Habitat changes:* Good sanitation in the home reduces cockroach numbers. Proper fertilization and growing conditions for shade trees help prevent borer infestations.

Mechanical Management

Mechanical devices are used to keep out or kill pests. These methods are frequently too labor intensive to be profitable commercially. In the relatively small areas of home landscapes, garden plots, and houses, however, mechanical devices may be very useful.

◆ *Handpicking:* removing insect pests by hand. Handpicking is useful in managing Colorado potato beetle adults and larvae, tomato hornworms, eastern tent caterpillars, fall webworms, and bagworm eggs.

◆ *Barriers:* keeping pests from reaching an area where damage can be caused. Tin cans and other barriers around young tomato plants can be used to keep out cutworms. Screening windows can keep out flies and other winged pests.

◆ *Devices:* using mechanical devices to manage insects. For example, fly swatters can be used to kill flies and other home-invading pests, and red sticky balls to capture apple maggots.

Ultrasonic devices have not been shown to be effective in repelling insect pests.

Plant Cover

Biological Management

Other living organisms are used to manage pests. Naturally occurring predators, parasites, and diseases are very effective in reducing pest populations. When we increase the numbers of these natural enemies, we are practicing biological management.

◆ Augment the habitat to provide favorable conditions for the natural enemy, thereby increasing its population. Allow fallen leaves and other debris to accumulate in such areas as the base of shrubs to provide overwintering sites for lady beetles and other predatory insects. Leave vegetation that harbors mite predators beneath fruit trees to help manage mite pests on the trees.

◆ Introduce additional natural enemies into the area. Natural enemies can be used as biological insecticides where they are introduced to manage specific pests. These natural enemies do not reproduce or survive in the environment, and therefore act as a one-shot insecticide. Examples of these enemies are *Steinernema carpocapsae* nematodes sprayed to manage sod webworms, army worms, and other turf pests; and bait shop minnows or other fish introduced into ornamental pools to manage mosquitoes.

Lady Beetle

Chemical Management

Chemical insecticides can be integral parts of many IPM programs. Pesticides are used to reduce pest populations below levels where they cause economic or aesthetic damage. Properly timed spot treatments with insecticides frequently provide adequate management so that additional applications are not necessary.

Insecticides

Much has been said about the effects of pesticides, particularly insecticides, on the health and well-being of the American people. We also are aware, however, that insects can destroy property and make life uncomfortable. Occasionally, we can avoid or reduce the destruction caused by some pests without using an insecticide. For many insects, we must rely on an insecticide to provide satisfactory management.

Safe Use of Insecticides

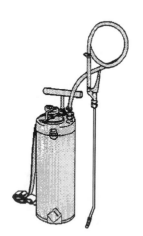

Hand Can Sprayer

By using insecticides and other pest-management tools carefully, we can enjoy reasonable freedom from insects without endangering ourselves, family, or pets. We must recognize that insecticides are designed to destroy one group of animals —insects—and can be harmful to other animals, including humans, if used irresponsibly. Insecticide users must handle, apply, and store insecticides safely to benefit from them without suffering from their dangers.

Tables 1 to 5 list insecticides that control insect pests of food, fabrics, structures, humans and animals, lawns, shrubs, trees, flowers, and vegetables. Suggestions include only the safest, most effective, and most available materials. Apply these insecticides and other pesticides according to directions on the container label. A resident may prefer to employ the services of a professional exterminator or custom applicator rather than to become involved in the selection and application of insecticides.

Insecticides and Their Names

The names used in the tables are the common chemical names, not the trade names, and as such may not be familiar to you. For instance, the common name for *Dursban* is *chlorpyrifos.* Tables 6 and 8 provide common, chemical, and/or trade names of insecticides. Table 7 is a conversion table for small quantities of insecticides.

Classification of Insecticides

Insecticides are classified for general use or restricted use by the U.S. Environmental Protection Agency. No insecticides in this chapter, except those listed for termites, have a restricted-use classification. A person wishing to use an insecticide classified for restricted use must be certified as a private or commercial applicator by the State of Illinois. Contact your local Extension office for details about applicator training programs.

Suggestions for the use of insecticides, effective from a practical standpoint, are based on available data. Many factors affect efficiency of management. These suggestions are subject to change without notification. Before using any insecticides, *always read the table introductions and footnotes,* which list precautions and other pertinent information.

For Your Protection

We urge you to consult the guidelines in the back of this book on using pesticides safely.

Sources of Information on Insects

Fact sheets describing the life history, habits, and damage of specific insects and nonchemical methods of management can be obtained from your local Extension office. These fact sheets are indicated by NHE number in the tables of this chapter.

Table 1. Management Suggestions for the Control of Insects in Vegetables

Insect	Crop	Suggestions	Insecticide
Aphids (NHE-47) Mites (NHE-58) Thrips	Most garden crops	Chemical. Apply on foliage to control the insects. Aphids and leafhoppers transmit plant diseases; early control is important. Mites web on the underside of leaves; apply insecticide to underside of leaves early, before extensive webbing occurs.	insecticidal soap malathion
Blister beetles (NHE-72) Cutworms (NHE-77) Flea beetles (NHE-36) Grasshoppers (NHE-74) Leafhoppers (NHE-22) Picnic beetles (NHE-40)	Most garden crops	Nonchemical. For cutworms, attach collars of paper, aluminum foil, or metal at planting for small numbers of plants. For picnic beetles, pick and destroy overripe or damaged vegetables. Chemical. Apply to base of plants at first sign of cutting by cutworms. Control grasshoppers in garden borders when hoppers are small.	carbaryl rotenone permethrin
All cabbage worms (NHE-45)	Cabbage and related crops, salad crops, leafy vegetables	Chemical. Presence of white butterflies signals start of infestation. Control worms when small. It is almost impossible to raise cole crops in Illinois without controlling these pests.	*Bacillus thuringiensis kurstaki*[a] permethrin
Hornworms (NHE-130) Fruitworms	Tomatoes	Nonchemical. Handpicking usually provide satisfactory control of hornworms. Without treatment, fruitworms usually damage less than 5% of the crop, so treatment may not be justified. Chemical. For fruitworms, apply to late-maturing tomatoes 3 or 4 times at 5- to 10-day intervals from small-fruit stage.	*Bacillus thuringiensis kurstaki*[a] carbaryl
Earworms (NHE-33)	Sweet corn	Nonchemical. If corn is harvested by the end of July in the northern half of Illinois, damage is usually avoided. Chemical. Apply at fresh-silk stage to early and late corn every 2 days, 4 or 5 times (carbaryl), or every 5 days, 2 or 3 times (permethrin).	carbaryl permethrin
Colorado potato beetles	Eggplant, potatoes, tomatoes	Nonchemical. Insects are usually present only in late May and June. Handpick larvae and adults off plants.	*Bacillus thuringiensis san diego*[a] or *tenebrionis*[a] carbaryl permethrin rotenone
Potato leafhoppers (NHE-22)	Potatoes, beans	Chemical. Apply 3 or 4 times at weekly intervals starting in late May or early June. Late potatoes and beans require additional treatments. These are the most serious pest of potatoes in Illinois.	carbaryl malathion permethrin
Bean leaf beetles (NHE-67)	Beans	Nonchemical. Plant late enough so that farmers' soybeans emerge before garden beans, making overwintering beetles less of a problem. Chemical. Leaves are riddled in early plantings. Apply once or twice as needed. Harvest is not affected if less than 20% of foliage is eaten. Also feed on pods.	carbaryl rotenone

[a]No time limitations

Table 1. Management Suggestions for the Control of Insects in Vegetables (cont.)

Insect	Crop	Suggestions	Insecticide
Mexican bean beetles	Beans	Chemical. Except for southern Illinois, a pest only of late beans. Harvest is not affected if less than 20% of foliage is eaten. Apply insecticide to underside of leaves.	carbaryl rotenone
Cucumber beetles (NHE-46)	Vine crops	Nonchemical. In the spring, cover plants with polyester row covers until blooming starts. Chemical. Apply as soon as beetles appear in spring. When blossoming begins, apply insecticide late in the day so as not to interfere with pollination by bees.	carbaryl rotenone
Corn rootworm beetles	Sweet corn	Chemical. Apply to green silks every 2 or 3 days while beetles are present and clipping silks. Cease treatments when silks turn brown.	carbaryl
Squash bug	Squash	Nonchemical. Handpick masses of reddish brown eggs on leaf undersides. Keep garden free of debris and lay down boards. During the day, remove boards and remove hiding bugs. Chemical. Treat bugs with sabedilla dust.	sabadilla
Squash vine borers (NHE-8)	Squash	Nonchemical. In the spring, cover plants with polyester row covers until blooming starts. Chemical. Make weekly applications to crowns and runners when plants begin to vine. Apply late in the day.	carbaryl
Corn borers	Sweet corn	Chemical. Apply 4 times every 3 days to whorl and ear zone of early corn when feeding appears on whorl leaves (carbaryl) or 2 or 3 times every 5 days (permethrin).	carbaryl permethrin
Slugs	All	Nonchemical. Reduce mulches, compost, and other organic matter. Chemical. Apply as bait to soil.	metaldehyde
Soil insects (including grubs, wireworms, root maggots)	All	Nonchemical. Cover the soil with screening along rows of root maggot–susceptible plants in spring. Chemical. Mix 6 fl oz of 25% diazinon emulsion in enough water to cover 1,000 sq ft, usually 2 to 3 gal. Rake into soil.	diazinon
Whiteflies	Tomato, squash, others	Chemical. Make 2 applications 5 to 7 days apart when large numbers are present.	insecticidal soap

Table 1a. Days Between Insecticide Application and Harvest

	Collards, kale, other leafy crops	Beans	Let-tuce	Cabbage, related crops	Sweet corn	Onions	Vine crops[a]	Toma-toes	Pump-kin	Egg-plant	Peas	Pota-toes
carbaryl	14	0	14	3	0	...	0	0	0	0	3	0
malathion	7	1	14	7	5	3	1	1	3	3	3	0
permethrin	...	...	...	1	1	...	...	...	...	3	...	7
rotenone	...	1	1	1	1	1	1	1	...	1	1	1

... = insecticide not labeled for that crop.
[a]To avoid bee kill, apply insecticides late in the day, after blossoms have closed.

Table 2. Management Suggestions for the Control of Insects in Flowers

Insect	Suggestions	Insecticide
Aphids, mealybugs, plant bugs, spittlebugs, lacebugs, scales (NHE-7, -114)	Spray foliage thoroughly. Repeat treatments may be needed.	acephate insecticidal soap malathion
Blister beetles (NHE-72)	Spray foliage. Repeat treatments may be needed.	carbaryl
Caterpillars, including painted lady, woolly-bears, and other leaf-feeding cater-pillars.	Spray foliage. Repeat treatments if needed.	acephate *Bacillus thuringiensis kurstaki* carbaryl
Cutworms (NHE-77)	Nonchemical. Small numbers of plants may be protected with collars of paper, aluminum foil, or metal. Chemical. Apply to soil at base of plants. Do not spray on plant foliage.	diazinon
Earwigs (NHE-142)	Spray foliage as needed. Do not spray blooms.	carbaryl
Grasshoppers (NHE-74)	Spray foliage, also adjacent grassy or weedy areas.	carbaryl malathion

NOTE: Use only one insecticide from those listed. Do not use oil-based sprays on plants. Do not use malathion on African violets. Do not use carbaryl on Boston ivy. Do not use diazinon on ferns. Repeated use of carbaryl foliage sprays may cause mite or aphid infestations to increase and to become damaging. Do not use insecticides during full bloom. Do not use dimethoate on chrysanthemums.

Table 2. Management Suggestions for the Control of Insects in Flowers (cont.)

Insect	Suggestions	Insecticide
Iris borer	Apply in April when leaves are 5 to 6 inches tall. Make only one application. Add a small amount of liquid detergent to spray mix to improve coverage on leaves.	dimethoate
Japanese beetles, and other leaf-feeding beetles	Spray foliage. Repeat treatments if needed.	acephate carbaryl
Mites	Spray foliage. Repeat in 5 days.	insecticidal soap
Plant bugs, leafhoppers	Spray foliage. Repeat treatments if needed.	acephate carbaryl
Slugs (NHE-84)	Nonchemical. Remove old leaves, stalks, poles, boards, and other debris where slugs like to hide and lay eggs. Copper edging repels slugs. Chemical. Apply as a bait to soil.	Mesurol bait metaldehyde bait
Stalk borers (NHE-24)	Spray foliage thoroughly and frequently.	acephate carbaryl
Thrips	Spray foliage carefully.	acephate azadirachtin carbaryl insecticidal soap
Whiteflies (NHE-136)	Spray foliage thoroughly. Repeat in 5 days.	insecticidal soap pyrethrin resmethrin

NOTE: Use only one insecticide from those listed. Do not use oil-based sprays on plants. Do not use malathion on African violets. Do not use carbaryl on Boston ivy. Do not use diazinon on ferns. Repeated use of carbaryl foliage sprays may cause mite or aphid infestations to increase and to become damaging. Do not use insecticides during full bloom. Do not use dimethoate on chrysanthemums.

Table 3. Management Suggestions for the Control of Insects in Trees and Shrubs

Insect	Suggestions[a]	Insecticide
Aphids (NHE-7)	Spray foliage thoroughly, with force, when aphids become numerous. Repeat as needed. Check for presence of lady beetles and other predators before spraying.	acephate diazinon insecticidal soap malathion
Bagworms (NHE-6)	Nonchemical. Handpicking of bags in winter and early spring reduces later infestations. Chemical. Spray foliage thoroughly. Apply in mid-June. Later sprays are less effective. For late spraying, use *Bacillus thuringiensis.*	acephate *Bacillus thuringiensis kurstaki* carbaryl malathion
Borers: Ash (NHE-145), lilac (NHE-145), peach tree	Nonchemical. Keep the tree healthy and vigorous, and avoid wounds or injury to the trunk. Prune out large lilac trunks. Chemical. Spray trunk and limbs in early to mid-June.	chlorpyrifos
Bronze birch (NHE-143)	Nonchemical. Keep trees watered during the summer. Keep trees healthy and vigorous. Chemical. Apply to trunk and limbs in mid-May. Repeat twice at 2-week intervals.	chlorpyrifos
Flatheaded apple tree, oak	Nonchemical. Keep trees healthy and vigorous and avoid trunk wounds. Chemical. Spray trunk and/or limbs in mid-May.	chlorpyrifos
Cankerworms (NHE-95)	Spray foliage when feeding or worms are first noticed in spring.	acephate *Bacillus thuringiensis kurstaki* carbaryl malathion
Eastern tent caterpillars	Nonchemical. Remove nests and destroy. Chemical. Spray when nests are first noticed.	same as for cankerworms
Elm leaf beetles (NHE-82)	Spray as soon as damage is noticed.	acephate *Bacillus thuringiensis san diego* or *tenebrionis* carbaryl
European pine shoot moths, Nantucket pine moths (NHE-83)	Spray ends of branches thoroughly in late June for European species and in mid-May for Nantucket species.	acephate dimethoate
Fall webworms	Nonchemical. Clip off and destroy infested branches. Chemical. Spray when first webs appear.	acephate *Bacillus thuringiensis kurstaki* carbaryl malathion

NOTE: Use only one insecticide of those listed. Do not use acephate on flowering crab, sugar maple, red maple, redbud, American elm, Lombardy poplar, or cottonwood. Do not use carbaryl on Boston ivy. Do not use diazinon on ferns or hibiscus. Do not use malathion on canaert red cedar.

[a]Treatment dates listed are for central Illinois. In southern Illinois, apply 2 weeks earlier; in northern Illinois, 2 weeks later.

Table 3. Management Suggestions for the Control of Insects in Trees and Shrubs (cont.)

Insect	Suggestions[a]	Insecticide
Galls (NHE-80, -81): Elm cockscomb, hickory, maple bladder, hackberry blister	Galls are not harmful to the tree. Treatments are not warranted.	
Cooley spruce, eastern spruce	Apply in late September or October or in early spring, just after budbreak.	diazinon malathion
Imported willow leaf beetles	Spray when larvae and foliage are small.	*Bacillus thuringiensis san diego* or *tenebrionis* carbaryl
Japanese beetle	Spray foliage. Repeat treatments if needed.	acephate carbaryl
Leaf miners: Boxwood, hawthorn, oak	Leaf miners usually do not harm the tree. Spray foliage thoroughly when miners first appear. Repeat treatment in 10 to 12 days. Do not use acephate on boxwood.	acephate diazinon malathion
Birch, holly	Spray foliage. Repeat treatment in 3 weeks.	acephate dimethoate
Mealybugs	Spray foliage thoroughly and with force. Repeat in 2 weeks.	acephate insecticidal soap malathion
Mimosa webworms (NHE-109)	Nonchemical. Physically remove and destroy nests. Chemical. Spray foliage thoroughly when first nests appear (June, July). A repeat treatment for second-generation larval feeding may be needed (August).	acephate *Bacillus thuringiensis kurstaki* malathion
Oak kermes	Spray foliage thoroughly about July 1 to kill the crawlers.	malathion
Periodical cicadas (NHE-113)	Nonchemical. Protect very young trees (less than 2-inch diameter) with screening around the trunk. Treatment not recommended on older trees because they will grow out of damage.	
Plant bugs	Spray when nymphs appear in spring.	acephate carbaryl malathion
Sawflies	Nonchemical. Handpicking is effective. Chemical. Spray as soon as worms or damage is evident.	carbaryl

NOTE: Use only one insecticide of those listed. Do not use acephate on flowering crab, sugar maple, red maple, redbud, American elm, Lombardy poplar, or cottonwood. Do not use carbaryl on Boston ivy. Do not use diazinon on ferns or hibiscus. Do not use malathion on canaert red cedar.

[a]Treatment dates listed are for central Illinois. In southern Illinois, apply 2 weeks earlier; in northern Illinois, 2 weeks later.

Table 3. Management Suggestions for the Control of Insects in Trees and Shrubs (cont.)

Insect	Suggestions[a]	Insecticide
Scales (NHE-100, -114, -144, -146)	Spray foliage thoroughly in early April for *Fletcher* and *European elm scales;* in late May for *pine needle, oystershell,* and *sweet gum scales;* in early June for *scurfy* and *euonymus scales;* in early July for *cottony maple, Juniper,* and *dogwood scales;* in mid-July for *spruce bud scale;* and again in August for *oystershell scale.*	acephate diazinon malathion petroleum oil diluted according to label as summer-oil spray
	Apply when plants are still dormant in late winter to control *cottony maple* (NHE-144), *Putnam, San Jose,* and *tulip tree scales.* Do not use on evergreens or hard maples. For *tulip tree scale,* a malathion spray in late September or in early spring is also effective.	petroleum oil diluted according to label as dormant spray
Spider mites	Spray when mites are numerous, usually midsummer. Concentrate spray on underside of the foliage. Repeat in 5 days.	dicofol insecticidal soap
Sycamore lace bugs	Spray when nymphs appear, usually in late May.	acephate carbaryl malathion
Thrips	Mainly on privet. Spray foliage thoroughly.	same as for aphids
Yellow-necked caterpillars	Nonchemical. Handpicking of colonies is effective. Chemical. Spray foliage when worms are small (July).	acephate *Bacillus thuringiensis kurstaki* carbaryl malathion
Zimmerman pine moths (NHE-83)	Spray trunk and branches in mid-April for young larvae and/or mid-August for adults and young larvae.	chlorpyrifos dimethoate

NOTE: Use only one insecticide of those listed. Do not use acephate on flowering crab, sugar maple, red maple, redbud, American elm, Lombardy poplar, or cottonwood. Do not use carbaryl on Boston ivy. Do not use diazinon on ferns or hibiscus. Do not use malathion on canaert red cedar.

[a]Treatment dates listed are for central Illinois. In southern Illinois, apply 2 weeks earlier; in northern Illinois, 2 weeks later.

Table 4. Management Suggestions for the Control of Insects in Lawns

Insect	Suggestions	Insecticide[a]
Ants (NHE-111); cicada killer and other soil-nesting wasps (NHE-79, -150)	Apply as spray or granules and water in thoroughly. For individual nests, pour diazinon in nest and cover with soil.	chlorpyrifos diazinon
Aphids (NHE-148)	Spray grass thoroughly.	acephate chlorpyrifos insecticidal soap
Armyworms, cutworms	Apply as sprays or granules. Use 5 to 10 gal of water per 1,000 sq ft.	carbaryl chlorpyrifos *Steinernema carpocapsae*
Bluegrass billbugs	For chlorpyrifos, apply as a spray in spring to lawn damaged in previous year. For both products, drench at high rate in July if damage is observed.	chlorpyrifos *Steinernema carpocapsae*
Chinch bugs	Spray infested areas where chinch bugs are present.	chlorpyrifos diazinon
Sod webworms (NHE-115)	As sprays, use at least 2.5 gal of water per 1,000 sq ft. Do not water for 72 hours after treatment. As granules, apply from fertilizer spreader. Webworms usually damage lawns in late July and in August.	carbaryl chlorpyrifos diazinon *Steinernema carpocapsae*
White grubs (NHE-104, -147), including annual white grubs, masked chafers, Japanese beetles, and green June beetles	Apply as spray or granules to small area and then apply ½" of water before treating another small area. Grub damage usually occurs in late August and in September. Apply imidicloprid only once in mid-July if adult beetle flight was high in areas where grub attack is common. Apply carbaryl only for green June beetle grubs.	bendiocarb carbaryl diazinon imidicloprid trichlorfon

[a]Use only one insecticide from those listed.

Table 5. Management Suggestions for the Control of Household Insects

Insect	Suggestions	Insecticide
Ants (NHE-111), including carpenter ants (NHE-10) *(nuisance pest)*	Nonchemical. Keep foods in tightly sealed containers or in the refrigerator. Most ants prefer sweets and fats. Practice good sanitation. Avoid leaving dirty dishes or food particles where they are accessible to ants. Caulk cracks and crevices in house foundation. Washing ant trails with detergent may confuse and greatly reduce ants. Carpenter ants excavate nests in damp wood indoors near current or old roof leaks and water and drain pipe leaks. Replace damaged wood containing nests. Chemical. Use diazinon or chlorpyrifos to spray completely around outside foundation and the adjacent 1 ft of soil. Apply an RTU spray to baseboards, cracks, and door thresholds. Apply boric acid in out-of-reach areas only. Place baits along areas where ants travel in nonfood areas. Spray carpenter ant nests with RTU spray.	*Outdoors:* chlorpyrifos diazinon *Indoors:* borate baits boric acid chlorpyrifos cyfluthrin cypermethrin diazinon d-phenothrin hydramethylnon baits permethrin propoxur propoxur baits resmethrin tralomethrin
Ants, pharaoh *(nuisance pest)*	Nonchemical. Follow suggestions given above for other ants. Apply petroleum jelly or double-sided tape to furniture legs to keep ants off furniture. Chemical. *Indoors:* Place baits near ant food, water sources, and other areas where ants are found. Treat for several weeks, replacing bait as it becomes dry.	boric acid baits methoprene baits
Boxelder bugs (NHE-9) *(nuisance pest)*	Nonchemical. Keep screens and other openings in good repair. Caulk all seams around windows and doors. *Indoors:* Remove the bugs by vacuuming. Chemical. Spray boxelder bugs on tree trunks, on foundation walls (insecticidal soap), under eaves, and in other areas where they gather. Use carbaryl on foliage and under trees where bugs are feeding.	carbaryl insecticidal soap
Bumblebees	Nonchemical. Avoid areas where bumblebees are prevalent. Mow areas near underground nests in evening when bees are less active. Wear protective clothing. Chemical. Apply diazinon according to label into underground nests and seal opening with soil. Wear protective clothing.	diazinon

NOTE: Those indicated as *nuisance pests* are primarily a problem due to their presence and are unlikely to cause harm to people, pets, buildings, or building contents. Thus, an acceptable option is to ignore them and not try to control them. Whenever possible, purchase specially prepared, ready-to-use (RTU) forms of insecticides for indoor use. Use only one insecticide from those listed. When preparing 1 gallon or more of a spray, follow the mixing directions on the pesticide label.

Table 5. Management Suggestions for the Control of Household Insects (cont.)

Insect	Suggestions	Insecticide
Carpenter bees	Nonchemical. In the fall, fill the holes, and paint or varnish the entire wood surface. Chemical. Dust entrances to nest with insecticide. Do not plug entrance.	carbaryl dust
Carpet beetles, clothes moths (NHE-87)	Nonchemical. Destroy all badly infested materials. If insulation is of plant or animal origin, remove it from the structure. Check for any dead animal or bird carcasses that may be in wall voids, chimneys, or fireplace areas. Keep accumulation of lint to a minimum, and vacuum thoroughly in areas where hair and other natural fibers gather. Remove all bird, insect, and rodent nests in the fall before cool weather. Place cleaned or washed woolens in insect-free chests that are tightly sealed or in plastic bags. Dry cleaning and laundering kill these pests. Chemical. Spray RTUs in edges of carpeting, baseboards, cracks, and crevices. Place cedar shavings, napthalene, or paradichlorobenzene in folds of woolens stored in airtight containers.	cedar shavings chlorpyrifos cyfluthrin cypermethrin diazinon d-phenothrin napthalene paradichlorobenzene permethrin resmethrin tralomethrin
Centipedes, millipedes, sowbugs (NHE-93) *(nuisance pest)*	Nonchemical. Correct situations where moist habitats occur, such as crawl spaces, poorly drained areas, and piles of trash, mulch, or compost. Remove indoors by vacuuming. Chemical. Apply diazinon or chlorpyrifos as an outside foundation spray. Millipedes are not effectively controlled with insecticides. *Indoors:* Use RTU spray according to label.	*Outdoors:* chlorpyrifos diazinon *Indoors:* chlorpyrifos diazinon d-phenothrin propoxur propoxur baits
Chiggers (NHE-127)	Nonchemical. Eliminate or mow breeding sites, especially briars, weeds, and other thick vegetation where there is an abundance of moisture and shade. Wear protective clothing, such as a long-sleeved shirt and trousers, shoes, and socks. Tuck pant-legs into boots or socks. Avoid sitting on the ground in either the lawn or brushy areas. Take a warm, soapy shower or bath immediately after returning from any infested areas. Chemical. Treat lawns, roadsides, and areas not mowed. For personal protection, a repellent such as DEET prevents attack.	DEET RTU diazinon

NOTE: Those indicated as *nuisance pests* are primarily a problem due to their presence and are unlikely to cause harm to people, pets, buildings, or building contents. Thus, an acceptable option is to ignore them and not try to control them. Whenever possible, purchase specially prepared, ready-to-use (RTU) forms of insecticides for indoor use. Use only one insecticide from those listed. When preparing 1 gallon or more of a spray, follow the mixing directions on the pesticide label.

Table 5. Management Suggestions for the Control of Household Insects (cont.)

Insect	Suggestions	Insecticide
Clover mites (NHE-2) *(nuisance pest)*	Nonchemical. Eliminate grass and other vegetation in a 1-ft band all the way around the house. Also make sure window and door seams are properly caulked and sealed to prevent entry by the mites. *Indoors:* Mites can be killed and removed by vacuuming and washing surfaces with soap and water. Chemical. Spray mites with insecticidal soap on outside walls and foundation. *Indoors:* Spray mites on surfaces and adjacent cracks and crevices with RTUs, or use indoor foggers.	*Outdoors:* insecticidal soap *Indoor sprays:* d-phenothrin fenvalerate tetramethrin *Indoor foggers:* fenvalerate permethrin pyrethrin resmethrin tetramethrin
Cluster flies (NHE-1) *(nuisance pest)*	Nonchemical. Seal cracks and openings around windows, eaves, and siding. Use fly screen over air-intake vents or air-conditioning systems. Seal off attic openings with screen or caulking. Chemical. Use dichlorvos resin strips in rooms or between storm and interior window panes. Fog lightly in rooms with RTU. Repeat spraying as needed.	dichlorvos resin strips d-phenothrin fenvalerate tetramethrin
Cockroaches: German (NHE-3), brown-banded (NHE-4), American and Oriental (NHE-5)	Nonchemical. Practice proper sanitation by keeping food properly sealed or stored in the refrigerator. Keep trash covered. Do not allow dirty dishes to accumulate. Clean frequently under refrigerator and stove, where food particles may accumulate. Eliminate hiding places, such as piles of newspapers, boxes, and papers. Caulk cracks and crevices in the foundation. Do not leave pet food out overnight. Chemical. Spray RTU into cracks and crevices where roaches hide. Treat under sink, refrigerator, and cabinets and on baseboards, etc. Treatment throughout home may be needed to control brown-banded roaches. Treatment may be supplemented with boric acid applied into out-of-sight and out-of-reach voids under cabinets and appliances.	abamectin boric acid chlorpyrifos cyfluthrin cypermethrin diazin d-phenothrin hydramethylnon bait hydroprene perme propoxur propoxur bait pyriproxifen resmethrin sulfluramid bait tralomethrin

NOTE: Those indicated as *nuisance pests* are primarily a problem due to their presence and are unlikely to cause harm to people, pets, buildings, or building contents. Thus, an acceptable option is to ignore them and not try to control them. Whenever possible, purchase specially prepared, ready-to-use (RTU) forms of insecticides for indoor use. Use only one insecticide from those listed. When preparing 1 gallon or more of a spray, follow the mixing directions on the pesticide label.

Table 5. Management Suggestions for the Control of Household Insects (cont.)

Insect	Suggestions	Insecticide
Crickets (NHE-137): Field, house, camel	Nonchemical. Cracks and crevices around windows and doors and in the foundation should be properly sealed and caulked. *Indoors:* Remove crickets by vacuuming. House lights attract both field and house crickets. Keep garbage cans clean, and empty them frequently. Keep firewood at least 1 to 2 ft from the foundation. Eliminate sources of moisture by fixing leaky pipes and modifying damp areas. Remove fallen leaves, bark mulch, and other organic debris near foundation. Chemical. Use diazinon or chlorpyrifos to spray completely around outside foundation and the adjacent 1 ft of soil. Apply an RTU spray to baseboards, cracks, and door thresholds.	*Outdoors:* chlorpyrifos diazinon *Indoors:* chlorpyrifos cyfluthrin cypermethrin diazinon d-phenothrin permethrin propoxur propoxur bait resmethrin tralomethrin
Drain flies (NHE-91) *(nuisance pest)*	Nonchemical. Practice proper sanitation. Clean out overflow drains, drain traps, and basement drains. Keep screens in good repair. Chemical. Use chemicals only after solving sanitation problems. Only after solving sanitation problems, pour rubbing alcohol or drain cleaner into overflow drain and main drain to eliminate maggots.	
Earwigs (NHE-142) *(nuisance pest)*	Nonchemical. Remove unessential plant debris, mulch, and boards from around buildings. Establish a zone of bare concrete or soil that will dry out. *Indoors:* Remove by vacuuming. Caulk cracks and crevices around windows and doors and in the foundation. Chemical. Apply diazinon or chlorpyrifos as an outside foundation spray. *Indoors:* Spray RTU into cracks and crevices.	*Outdoors:* chlorpyrifos diazinon *Indoors:* chlorpyrifos cyfluthrin cypermethrin diazinon d-phenothrin permethrin propoxur propoxur bait resmethrin tralomethrin

NOTE: Those indicated as *nuisance pests* are primarily a problem due to their presence and are unlikely to cause harm to people, pets, buildings, or building contents. Thus, an acceptable option is to ignore them and not try to control them. Whenever possible, purchase specially prepared, ready-to-use (RTU) forms of insecticides for indoor use. Use only one insecticide from those listed. When preparing 1 gallon or more of a spray, follow the mixing directions on the pesticide label.

Table 5. Management Suggestions for the Control of Household Insects (cont.)

Insect	Suggestions	Insecticide
Elm leaf beetles (NHE-82) *(nuisance pest)*	Nonchemical. Seal cracks and crevices around windows and other openings to prevent entry. *Indoors:* Remove by vacuuming. Chemical. Spray nearby Chinese elm trees during the summer to reduce the number of beetles that come into homes in the fall.	*Bacillus thuringiensis san diego* or *tenebrionis* carbaryl
Fleas (NHE-107) *(Refer to section on pets, following this table.)*	Nonchemical. *Indoors:* With hot, soapy water, frequently launder pet bedding and rugs frequented by pets. Vacuum thoroughly to remove lint and dust around baseboards and cracks where flea eggs and larvae accumulate. Thoroughly clean furniture in areas pets tend to frequent. *Outdoors:* Eliminate vegetation that serves as a harborage for the native mammal population (carriers of fleas). Prevent pets from resting under the house, and exclude mammals by screening attic and eave entrances. Chemical. *Pets:* Replace flea collars on pets about every 3 months. Some pets are allergic. Dust pets directly as needed. *Indoors:* Dust areas inside and outside the home where pets rest. For infestations in the home, spray RTU on carpets and rugs and into cracks and crevices where fleas are observed. Follow label directions. Vacuum rugs and upholstered furniture thoroughly about 30 minutes after spraying. *Do not use diazinon EC indoors. Outdoors:* Apply to lawn.	*Pets:* carbaryl dust naled *Outdoors:* diazinon *Indoors:* methoprene + permethrin, pyrethrin, or tetramethrin pyriproxifen
Flies (NHE-16): Houseflies, gnats, midges	Nonchemical. Proper sanitation is important. Dispose of refuse frequently and prevent the accumulation of rotting or decaying vegetation. Keep screens in good repair. Fly strips and fly swatters also can be effective. Chemical. Use malathion to spray around garbage cans and other resting sites. Apply fine mist or fog of RTU.	*Outdoors:* malathion *Indoors:* d-phenothrin tetramethrin
Honey bees (NHE-141)	Nonchemical. Caulk cracks and crevices during the winter or early spring to prevent nest building. Seal attic openings, air-intake vents, and air-conditioning systems with window screening. Chemical. Dust openings to nest in partitions. Remove nests and honey, and destroy them. Treat nests at dusk or dawn. Wear protective clothing.	carbaryl dust

NOTE: Those indicated as *nuisance pests* are primarily a problem due to their presence and are unlikely to cause harm to people, pets, buildings, or building contents. Thus, an acceptable option is to ignore them and not try to control them. Whenever possible, purchase specially prepared, ready-to-use (RTU) forms of insecticides for indoor use. Use only one insecticide from those listed. When preparing 1 gallon or more of a spray, follow the mixing directions on the pesticide label.

Table 5. Management Suggestions for the Control of Household Insects (cont.)

Insect	Suggestions	Insecticide
Lice (NHE-105): Human, head, crab, body	Nonchemical. Practice proper personal hygiene. Avoid using other individuals' combs, hats, towels, and hairbrushes. Bedding and clothing should be changed and washed frequently. Sanitation of locker rooms and proper laundering helps reduce the incidence of lice. Crab louse is usually transmitted through intimate sexual contact. Chemical. Apply to body according to label directions. Do not get shampoo or chemical in the eyes. Consult a physician if eyes are affected.	Kwell shampoo pyrethrin
Mites, bird *(Refer to section on pets, following this table.)*	Nonchemical. Remove empty bird nests on the building. Kill mites with soap and water where nest was located, on windowsills and frames, and on interior surfaces. Chemical. Spray building where nest was located. Spray window sills and frames.	d-phenothrin fenvalerate tetramethrin
Mites, human: Human scabies, human itch mites (NHE-135)	Chemical. Consult a physician. Follow label directions.	Kwell lotion (available only by a physician's prescription) pyrethrin
Mosquitoes (NHE-94, -132)	Nonchemical. Keep screens in good repair. Cover flues and chimneys during the summer months. Eliminate resting places such as tall grass, weeds, shrubbery, and vines from around the home. Eliminate rainwater-collecting items such as old tires, pans, cans, and buckets. Weekly, drain plastic swimming pools and birdbaths. Provide for proper water drainage around the foundation of the home. When visiting mosquito-infested areas, wear protective clothing to prevent bites. If small garden ponds are present, use Top minnows, *Gambusia* sp., or *Bacillus thuringiensis israelensis*. *"Bug zappers" and ultrasonic devices have not proved to be particularly effective in controlling mosquitoes and other noxious flying insects.* Chemical. Spray tall grass, areas around doorways, and other resting sites. Use a repellent like DEET when entering mosquito-infested areas.	*Outdoors:* *Bacillus thuringiensis israelensis* DEET RTU d-phenothrin malathion resmethrin

NOTE: Those indicated as *nuisance pests* are primarily a problem due to their presence and are unlikely to cause harm to people, pets, buildings, or building contents. Thus, an acceptable option is to ignore them and not try to control them. Whenever possible, purchase specially prepared, ready-to-use (RTU) forms of insecticides for indoor use. Use only one insecticide from those listed. When preparing 1 gallon or more of a spray, follow the mixing directions on the pesticide label.

Table 5. Management Suggestions for the Control of Household Insects (cont.)

Insect	Suggestions	Insecticide
Pantry and cereal pests (NHE-11): Grain beetles, indianmeal moths, flour beetles	Nonchemical. Discard infested packages. Thoroughly clean and vacuum food cabinets and shelves. Keep dry food in tightly sealed containers. Freezing food not meant for humans to eat for 3 to 4 days kills eggs and larvae. Chemical. None.	
Pomace flies, fruit flies	Remove sources of infestation, such as apples, tomatoes, potatoes, onions, and other stored fruits and vegetables. Make sure drains and garbage disposals are clean. Trap remaining flies with commercial traps or long-necked bottles such as wine bottles laid on their sides, containing a little wine or a mixture of water, sugar, and yeast.	
Powder-post beetles (NHE-85)	Nonchemical. Avoid buying furniture or wood products that have not been stained, varnished, or properly dried. Properly paint or varnish new wood items to seal pores and to prevent egg laying. Chemical. Use chlorpyrifos or boric acid to paint or spray infested unfinished wood. Follow label directions.	borate chlorpyrifos
Silverfish (NHE-86) (*nuisance pest*)	Nonchemical. Alter the physical environment of the infested area by reducing the humidity. Reduce harborage sites by caulking cracks and crevices. Eliminate silverfish food sources by storing books, papers, and linens in tightly sealed containers or cabinets. Chemical. Spray runways, baseboards, closets, and places where pipes go through the walls. Repeat treatments in 4 weeks if needed. Apply boric acid in out-of-reach areas only.	boric acid chlorpyrifos cyfluthrin cypermethrin diazinon d-phenothrin permethrin propoxur resmethrin tralomethrin
Spiders (NHE-17, -116)	Nonchemical. Keep screens and other openings in good repair. Caulk all seams around windows and doors. Spiders are considered beneficial, as they are predators of insects and other small animals. *Indoors:* Remove by vacuuming. Chemical. Use diazinon or chlorpyrifos to spray completely around outside foundation and the adjacent 1 ft of soil. Apply RTU spray to baseboard, cracks, and door thresholds. *Do not use diazinon or chlorpyrifos EC indoors.*	*Outdoors:* chlorpyrifos diazinon *Indoors:* chlorpyrifos cyfluthrin cypermethrin diazinon d-phenothrin permethrin propoxur resmethrin tralomethrin

NOTE: Those indicated as *nuisance pests* are primarily a problem due to their presence and are unlikely to cause harm to people, pets, buildings, or building contents. Thus, an acceptable option is to ignore them and not try to control them. Whenever possible, purchase specially prepared, ready-to-use (RTU) forms of insecticides for indoor use. Use only one insecticide from those listed. When preparing 1 gallon or more of a spray, follow the mixing directions on the pesticide label.

Table 5. Management Suggestions for the Control of Household Insects (cont.)

Insect	Suggestions	Insecticide
Springtails (NHE-70) *(nuisance pest)*	Nonchemical. Eliminate moist areas around the home where mulch and rotting vegetation are present. Keep use of outside lights to a minimum. Keep screens and doors in good repair. Allow potting soil of houseplants to dry out between waterings. *Indoors:* Reduce humidity and moisture leaks in infested areas. Chemical. *Outdoors:* Spray soil next to the house, especially grassy, moist areas.	*Outdoors:* chlorpyrifos diazinon
Swimming pool insects (NHE-103) *(nuisance pest)*	Nonchemical. Keep outside light to a minimum. Maintain proper chlorine balance in the pool. Cover pool when not in use. Chemical. None.	Do *not* add insecticides to pool water.
Termites (NHE-57)	Nonchemical. Remove termite tubes connecting the soil to wood sources. Eliminate wood-to-soil contacts. Ventilate damp areas such as crawl spaces for proper drying. Use treated wood when landscaping or constructing outside structures. Cedar and redwood are somewhat resistant; termites prefer hardwoods. Chemical. Control by pest control operator (exterminator) is recommended.	bifenthrin (Biflex) borate chlorpyrifos (Dursban T.C.*, Equity*, Tenure*) cypermethrin* (Demon, Prevail) fenvalerate* (Tribute) hexaflumeron* (Recruit bait) hydramethylnon* (Subterfuge)[a] imidicloprid (primise) permethrin* (Dragnet, Torpedo) sulfluramid* (First Line bait)
Ticks (NHE-56): Brown dog ticks, American dog ticks, lone star ticks, black-legged ticks (deer tick) *(Refer to section on pets, following this table.)*	Nonchemical. Keep vegetation, weeds, and brush mowed and clean. Avoid areas where ticks are known to be present. Wear long-sleeved shirt and trousers when visiting infested areas; tuck pant-legs into socks. Check for ticks on skin or clothing every few hours. Remove attached ticks by grasping with tweezers where mouthparts are attached to the skin and pulling slowly. Vacuum baseboards and cracks and crevices thoroughly to destroy eggs and immatures. Chemical. Apply spray to lawns, fencerows, roadsides, and areas not regularly mowed. Dust pets directly as needed, according to label instructions. Dust baseboards, cracks, and crevices around pet bedding. Use a repellent like DEET when entering tick-infested areas. Permethrin can be used on clothing.	*Outdoors:* carbaryl malathion tetrachlorvinphos 50WP *Pets:* carbaryl dust tetrachlorvinphos dust *Humans:* DEET RTU permethrin

NOTE: Those indicated as *nuisance pests* are primarily a problem due to their presence and are unlikely to cause harm to people, pets, buildings, or building contents. Thus, an acceptable option is to ignore them and not try to control them. Whenever possible, purchase specially prepared, ready-to-use (RTU) forms of insecticides for indoor use. Use only one insecticide from those listed. When preparing 1 gallon or more of a spray, follow the mixing directions on the pesticide label.

*Restricted-use pesticide (RUP) or marketed only to professionals. Restricted-use pesticides are too hazardous to people or the environment to be available to the general public. One must be a certified pesticide applicator or be supervised by a certified pesticide applicator to purchase or apply a restricted-use pesticide.

[a]At time of publication, not yet available.

Table 5. Management Suggestions for the Control of Household Insects (cont.)

Insect	Suggestions	Insecticide
Wasps (NHE-141), hornets, yellow jackets	**Nonchemical.** Keep garbage cleaned up and properly covered. Avoid indiscriminate killing of wasps, hornets, and yellow jackets, as they are considered beneficial. If picnicking, keep food properly covered or sealed. Avoid areas where yellow jackets are prevalent. Keep overripe fruit and vegetables cleaned up and away from human activity. Caulk cracks and crevices during the winter or early spring to prevent yellow jacket nests, but do not caulk opening of active nest. **Chemical.** For nests below ground, apply diazinon according to label, and seal opening with soil. Dust openings to wasp nest in partitions with carbaryl. Spray outdoor, aboveground wasp and hornet nests with RTUs. Remove nests and destroy them. Treat nests at dusk or dawn. Wear protective clothing.	bendiocarb carbaryl dust chlorpyrifos diazinon d-phenothrin propoxur resmethrin

Managing Pests of Pets
Fleas

Fleas are a common pest of both dogs and cats. At times, population levels can become high enough that humans in the household may be fed upon, particularly if the pet has been absent for a day or two. Children are often quite sensitive to flea saliva.

Flea

The life cycle of fleas infesting dogs and cats (primarily the species called the cat flea) starts with tiny white eggs, released by the female fleas while feeding, which drop through the hair of the host and fall to the ground or floor. The small, white maggotlike larvae that hatch from these eggs feed on partially digested blood feces from adult fleas and decomposing organic matter. The pupae, which look like large grains of sand, are impervious to treatment by most insecticides. The adults choose a cat or dog for a permanent host and generally only leave the host to go to another animal that is in direct contact with the original host.

Both adult fleas that have not eaten a blood meal and pupae can go for long periods of time without hosts' being available. Pupae commonly remain inactive until vibrations from a possible host cause them to emerge as hungry adults. This is why it is common to have large numbers of hungry fleas jumping on people and animals after a home has been vacant for one or more weeks. (To avoid major problems with this, try sending your pet into the house first.)

All stages, except the eggs, have special adaptations to prevent themselves from being moved from where they are. Larvae have hairs that can become entwined in carpet. The irregular shape and somewhat sticky surface of the pupae help them stay in place. And the adults have a variety of tiny spines that they use to hold on tightly to the host's hair. As a result of these and other aspects of the biology of these pests, an integrated approach is required for successful control. Even an integrated approach will not guarantee complete or permanent success for people whose pets contact other animals or are allowed freedom of movement outdoors, but such an approach will help alleviate the problem enormously.

Indoor Environment

Frequent vacuuming is an integral part of an indoor flea-control program. Vacuuming not only helps remove flea eggs and larvae but also lifts and dries the carpet fibers, which allows the insecticide to reach down to the base. Vacuuming also stimulates the fleas to hatch from the cocoons and climb to the top of the carpet, where they are susceptible to insecticidal applications. Vacuuming should include areas under sofas, beds, and chairs where larvae may have crawled. In addition to the carpeting, seat cushions and pillows should be thoroughly vacuumed as well. After each vacuuming, the bag should be removed and discarded.

After vacuuming, the indoor environment should be treated with an insect growth regulator (methoprene, fenoxycarb) combined with an insecticide that will be effective against the adults. Insect growth regulators prevent flea larvae from developing into adults. In heavily infested homes, additional treatments are necessary because fleas continue to emerge from cocoons that are resistant to the treatments. Application of insecticides in the home can be accomplished by broadcast treatment (pumps or sprays) onto carpets and into cracks and crevices. Special efforts also should be directed to areas where the pet spends a lot of time, because eggs and larvae accumulate there. After the carpet has dried, vacuum a second time to remove additional fleas that were stimulated to hatch.

Outdoor Environment

Outdoors, flea development occurs only in areas that are moist and protected from sunlight. Thus, it is not necessary to treat the entire lawn but, rather, to concentrate on shaded, moist areas where pets tend to lie—under porches, beneath trees and shrubs, and in doghouses. These areas should be raked and all organic debris removed. These "hot spots" should then be sprayed with products that contain a residual insecticide and an insect growth regulator.

On the Animal

Many products are available to treat pets for fleas. These products come in many formulations, including shampoos, mists, sprays, powders, mousses, dips, collars, and systemics. Recently, a new once-a-month insect growth regulator (lufeneuron) was approved for oral use in dogs and cats. Most registered flea-control products are effective for killing fleas on the animal. It is best to consult with your veterinarian about which type of products would work best in your individual flea-control program.

The control of fleas on pets requires an integrated approach. Not only must the pet be treated, but both the indoor and outdoor environment as well. Successful flea control will happen only if all three are treated *at the same time.* The types of control materials that you use should be modified for your specific needs. For example, you might consider using different insecticides if you have an infant than what you would use if only adults lived in your home.

Ticks

In Illinois, four species of ticks are commonly found on household pets. Three of these (the American dog tick, the lonestar tick, and the black-legged or deer tick) are most likely to be acquired away from the household, while the fourth, the brown dog tick, has adapted to living in kennels, homes, and doghouses without reverting to another environment.

The differences are quite easy to understand when you realize that the primary host of the brown dog tick is the dog, whereas the other species prefer different-sized hosts at different life stages and digest their bloodmeals while hidden by soil or leaf litter. In contrast, the brown dog tick frequently climbs after feeding and can be found at the tops of curtains, behind cove moldings, and even in furniture. The brown dog tick does not survive cold weather as well as the other three species, at least partially because it does not cover itself in any insulatory material.

These ticks all have the same type of life cycle. The adults lay from a few hundred to several thousand eggs that hatch into a motile six-legged stage called a larva. This larval stage will take a single bloodmeal, spending 3 to 5 days feeding on a host before dropping off to digest its meal and then molting to an eight-legged stage called a nymph. The nymph feeds for a little longer than the larva, 5 to 7 days, before dropping off the host to molt into adults.

The eight-legged adult stage comes in two somewhat different forms according to sex. Before feeding, the female has a small, colored "shield" that does not cover the whole body. The male, often half the size of the female, has a shield that covers the entire body. In some tick species, the male takes very little if any blood and simply spends most of its time on a host looking for females. After feeding, a mated female lays her eggs in a protected site, sometimes digging under litter or through loose soil to find a good spot.

When looking for hosts, ticks of all stages frequently climb to the top of grasses and wait for a host to come along. When motion or smell leads a tick to "think" that a host is near, it waves at least one pair of legs in the air, hoping for contact by the host it has sensed.

Worldwide, many diseases are transmitted by ticks. In Illinois, three relatively rare diseases can be acquired from ticks. Lyme disease, the most common, is transmitted by the black-legged tick. There have never been as many as 100 cases of human Lyme disease confirmed in a single year in Illinois. Rocky Mountain spotted fever is even more rare in Illinois. It is transmitted by the American dog tick. Another disease transmitted by both the black-legged and the lone star tick has recently been identified as human granulocytic ehrlichiosis. These diseases are not a threat to most people, and all are treatable by physicians.

Tick

Tick Removal

Ticks can be removed, using forceps or tweezers, by pushing the arms of the forceps under the part of the tick that is embedded in the skin and lifting straight up (do not twist) slowly and carefully. This method accomplishes two things by keeping the tick intact: (1) It makes the tick more easily identified by a professional, and (2) it prevents parts from being left in the host to start secondary infections. Anyone who becomes ill after suffering tick bites should inform a physician, keep the tick in alcohol, and have it identified by a professional entomologist.

Indoor Management

Because the brown dog tick is the only species likely to be found indoors (and it actively seeks cracks and crevices to hide in), management may be a long-term project. Do not be surprised if it takes up to 6 months to eliminate this pest because eggs of this species may take nearly that long to hatch. Various formulations of the compounds listed in the following chart are available for use in your home. Read the labels carefully before buying and again before using to be sure that the chemicals are compatible with your needs. Apply the materials around animal quarters and in cracks and crevices where ticks might hide (baseboards, door frames, windowsills) as well as the floor. Only 5 percent carbaryl dust should be used in the animal's quarters. For all other materials, change the animal's bedding after treatment. Until treated areas dry, keep children and pets away from them.

Outdoor Management

Both the American dog tick and the black-legged tick (deer tick) migrate to the edges of lawns. Homeowners may wish to spray or dust with one of the acaricides listed in the following chart. Read the label instructions carefully before purchasing and again before use to make sure these compounds are compatible with your needs. Apply these compounds in and under shrubs and bushes, as well as in the grass. Keep children and pets away from the treated area until it is dry.

Kennels

You may wish to consult your veterinarian before using an acaricide in kennels. Puppies are frequently more susceptible to toxic substances than older dogs, and puppies are more likely to seek places where ticks may be concentrated following treatment. Treatments for ticks on dogs are available at your veterinarian's office, at pet stores, and in drugstores and hardware stores. The active ingredients of these treatments are generally pyrethrins, malathion, and carbaryl (Sevin).

Acaricides for Use Indoors

Acaricide	Formulations
carbaryl (Sevin)	5% dust
chlorpyrifos (Dursban)	22.4% emulsifiable concentrate
diazinon	47.5% emulsifiable concentrate
propoxur (Baygon)	0.5% and 1% sprays (ready-to-use)
pyrethrins	many formulations, some ready-to-use

Acaricides for Use Outdoors

Acaricide	Formulation
chlorpyrifos	6%/lb and 22.4% emulsifiable concentrate
diazinon	many formulations
malathion	57% emulsifiable concentrate
pyrethrins	many formulations
Rabon	50% wettable powder

Mites

Various mites infect our companion animals. These pests include burrowing mange mites (*Sarcoptes* sp., *Notoedres* sp.), hair follicle mites (*Demodex* sp.), fur mites (*Cheyletiella*), and ear mites (*Otodectes* sp.). Mites are microscopic arthropods whose entire life cycle is spent on the host. Mites can be quite irritating to the host. Signs of mite infestation can include scratching, hair loss, head shaking and tilting, redness of the skin, and secondary bacterial infections. Some of the mites of our pets can temporarily infect humans, causing an itchy skin rash. When bird nests in your yard or attic are abandoned, the mites that infest these nests may seek alternative blood sources. The resulting infections are usually temporary on humans, but pet birds should be taken to a veterinarian.

Products are available to treat mites on pets. The treatment varies, depending on the type of mite present. If you suspect mites, have your pet checked and treated by your veterinarian.

Table 6. Names of Insecticides

Common name	Trade name	Chemical name
abamectin	Black Flag Roach Ender	Avermectin B, a mixture of avermectins
acephate	Acephate, Orthene	O, S-dimethyl acetylphosphoramidothioate
azadirachtin	Bioneem, Natural Guard Neem	botanical insecticide from the Neem tree
Bacillus thuringiensis israelensis	Mosquito Attack	bacterial toxin
Bacillus thuringiensis kurstaki	B.t., Caterpillar Attack, Dipel, Ortho *B.t.* Biospray, Thuricide	bacterial toxin
Bacillus thuringiensis san diego or *tenebrionis*	M-Trak, Trident	bacterial toxin
bendiocarb	Ficam, Intercept	2,2-dimethyl-1,3-benzodioxol-4-yl methylcarbamate
borate	Bora-Care, Tim-bor	disodium octaborate tetrahydrate
boric acid	Roach Powder Roach Prufe, Terro Ant Bait,	boric acid
carbaryl	Hi-Yield Rose, Flower, and Vegetable Dust; Sevin	1-naphthyl methylcarbamate
chlorpyrifos	Dursban, Ferti-lome Borer Killer	O, O-diethyl O-(3,5,6-trichloro-2-pyridyl) phosphorothioate
cyfluthrin	Tempo	Cyano (4-fluoro-3-phenoxyphenyl) methyl 3-(2,2-dichloroethenyl)-2,2-dimethylcyclopropanecarboxylate
cypermethrin	Demon	a-Cyano-3-phenoxybenzyl cis, trans-3-(2,2-dichlorovinyl)-2, 2-dimethylcyclopropanecarboxylate
DEET	Cutter's, Off	N, N-diethyl-m-toluamide

NOTE: This table lists the common names of insecticides used in the tables, followed by the commercial trade names and the chemical names. Some products may be available under a variety of trade names that are not listed below. Be sure to read the label. The label on the container always lists these products by the common name or chemical name. Additional trade names for household insect control are listed in Table 8.

Table 6. Names of Insecticides (cont.)

Common name	Trade name	Chemical name
diazinon	Ferti-lome Bug Blaster Lawn/Garden Insect Killer, Ferti-lome Rose Spray, Ferti-lome Triple-Action, Spectracide	O-diethyl O-(2-isopropyl-4-methyl-6-pyrimidyl) phosphorothioate
dichlorvos	DDVP, Vapona	2,2-dichlorovinyl dimethyl phosphate
dicofol	Kelthane	1,1-Bis(chlorophenyl)-2,2,2-trichloroethanol
dimethoate	Cygon, Ferti-lome Ornamental & Evergreen Spray	O, O-dimethyl S-(N-methyl carbamoyl methyl) phosphorodithioate
d-phenothrin	Sumithrin	3-phenoxybenzyl d-cis/trans 2,2-dimethyl-3-(2-methylpropenyl) cyclopropanecarboxylate
d-trans allethrin	Black Flag Roach Ender	allyl homolog of cinerin I
fenvalerate	Pyrid, Tribute	cyano (3-phenoxyphenyl) methyl 4-chloro-(1methylethyl) benzeneacetate
hydramethylnon	Combat	tetrahydro-5,5-dimethyl-2(IH)-pyrimidinone (3-[4-(trifluoromethyl)phenyl]-1-(2-[4-(trifluoromethyl)phenyl]-ethenyl)-2-propenylidene)hydrazone
hydroprene	Gencor	ethyl-3,7,11-trimethyl dodeca-2,4 dienoate
imidicloprid	Merit, others	l-[(6-chloro-3-pyridinyl)methyl]-N-nitro-2-imidazolidinimine
insecticidal soap	Attack, M-Pede, Safer's Insecticidal Soap	potassium salts of fatty acids
malathion	Cython, Mal-A-Cide	diethyl mercaptosuccinate, S-ester with O, O-dimethyl phosphorothioate
metaldehyde	Bug-Geta, Ferti-lome Snail & Slug Bait, Hi-Yield Snail & Slug Pellets	2,4,6,8-tetramethyl-1,3,5,7-tetroxocane
methoprene	Pharorid, Precor	isopropyl-11-methoxy-3,7,11-trimethyl-2,4 dodecadienoate
naled	Dibrom	1,2-dibromo-2,2-dichloroethyl dimethyl phosphate
naphthalene	Moth crystals	naphthalene
paradichlorobenzene	Moth crystals	1,4-dichlorobenzene

NOTE: This table lists the common names of insecticides used in the tables, followed by the commercial trade names and the chemical names. Some products may be available under a variety of trade names that are not listed below. Be sure to read the label. The label on the container always lists these products by the common name or chemical name. Additional trade names for household insect control are listed in Table 8.

Table 6. Names of Insecticides (cont.)

Common name	Trade name	Chemical name
permethrin	Intercept-H&G, Permanone, Spectracide Bug Stop	(3-phenoxyphenyl)methyl (I) cis/trans-ethenyl-2,2-dimethylcyclopropane-carboxylate
petroleum oil	Ferti-lome Scalecide; horticultural spray oil; Superior Oil Spray; Volck Oil Spray, Dormant & Summer Oil Spray	petroleum oil
propoxur	Baygon	2-(1-methylethoxy) phenyl methylcarbamate
pyrethrin	Ferti-lome Quik-Kill, Ferti-lome Red Spider Mite RTU, Ferti-lome Time Release Indoor/Outdoor Insect Control, Ortho Rose & Flower Insect Spray, Pyrenone	principally from plant species *Chrysanthemum cinariaefolium*
pyriproxyfen	Admiral, Ferti-lome Barren,	2-[1-methyl-2-(4-phenoxyphenoxy)ethoxy] pyridine
resmethrin	Chryson, Ferti-lome Whitefly & Mealybug Killer, SBP-1282	(5-benzyl-3-furyl) methyl 2,2 dimethyl-3-(2-methylpropenyl) cyclopropanecarboxylate
rotenone	Natural Guard & Ferti-lome Rose, Floral & Vegetable Dust; Rotenone	principally from the plants Derris and Cubé
sabadilla	Sabadilla	principally from the plant *Schoenocaalon*
Steinernema carposapsae	Biosafe	insect-attacking nematode
sulfluramid	Raid Max Roach Bait	N-ethyl perfluorooctane sulfonamide
tetrachlorvinphos	Rabon	2-chloro-1-(2,4,5-trichlorophenyl) vinyl dimethyl phosphate
tetramethrin	Neo-Pynamin, Phthalthrin	(1-cyclohexene-1,2-dicarboximido)-methyl 2,2-dimethyl-3-(2-methylpropenyl)-cyclopropanecarboxylate
tralomethrin	Scout	(tetrabromoethyl)-2,2-dimethylcyclopropanecarboxylic acid
trichlorfon	Dylox	dimethyl (2,2,2-trichloro-1-hydroxyethyl) phosphonate

NOTE: This table lists the common names of insecticides used in the tables, followed by the commercial trade names and the chemical names. Some products may be available under a variety of trade names that are not listed below. Be sure to read the label. The label on the container always lists these products by the common name or chemical name. Additional trade names for household insect control are listed in Table 8.

Table 7. Conversion Table for Small Quantities of Insecticide

1 level tablespoon = 3 level teaspoons
1 fluid ounce = 2 tablespoons
1 cup = 8 fluid ounces or 16 tablespoons
1 pint = 2 cups
1 quart = 2 pints or 32 fluid ounces
1 gallon = 4 quarts or 128 fluid ounces

Table 8. Common and Trade Names of Ready-to-Use Household Insecticides

Common name	Trade name
abamectin	Black Flag Roach Ender
bendiocarb	Bengal Wasp & Hornet Killer
	Green Thumb Wasp & Hornet Killer
borate	Pic Liquid Bait Ant Killer
	Terro Ant Killer II
boric acid	Enforcer Roach Ridd
	Enoz Roach Away
	Hi-Yield Roach Powder
	Natural Guard Gardening Natures Way
	Pic Ant Control System
	Pic Ant Trap
	Roachbusters
	Roach Prufe
	Victor Liquid Ant Killing System
chlorpyrifos	Black Flag Ant Control System
	Black Flag Roach & Ant Killer (+ allethrin)
	Bonide Home Pest Control Concentrate
	d-Con Crawling Bug Killer (+ allethrin)
	Dursban
	Ferti-lome Kill-A-Bug Indoor/Outdoor Insect Control
	Green Thumb Home Pest Insect Killer
	Hi-Yield Kill-A-Bug RTU
	Hi-Yield Termite & Soil Insect Killer
	K-Gro Home Pest Insect Control
	K-Rid Ant & Roach Killer (+ pyrethrin)
	K-Rid Home Insect Killer
	K-Rid Roach & Flea Fogger
	K-Rid Wasp & Hornet Killer (+ allethrin)
	Meijer Ant Killer Spray
	Meijer Home Insect Killer
	Mr. Scott's Do It Yourself Pest Control
	NU-MRK Ant & Roach Killer (+ resmethrin)

NOTE: This table lists the trade names of many of the ready-to-use (RTU) household insecticides. Insecticides should be selected by the insecticide listed in the heading under "common name," not those in parentheses in this table. The insecticides listed in parentheses will add some control to the situation, but the one in the heading will be as effective or more effective in controlling the pest. Some products may be available under trade names that are not listed above. Trade names are capitalized; common names are not.

Table 8. Common and Trade Names of Ready-to-Use Household Insecticides (cont.)

Common name	Trade name
chlorpyrifos (cont.)	Ortho Ant, Flea & Cricket Spray
	Ortho Ant-Stop Ant Killer
	Ortho Flea-B-Gon Flea & Tick Killer
	Ortho Home Pest Insect Control
	Ortho-Klor Ant Killer Dust
	Ortho-Klor Soil Insect & Termite Killer
	Pulvex Flea & Tick Spray (+ pyrethrin)
	Raid Ant Baits
	Raid Ant Controller
	Raid Crack & Crevice Roach Foam
	Raid Flea Killer Plus Yard Spray
	Raid Home Insect Killer
	Raid Liquid Roach & Ant Killer (+ pyrethrin)
	Raid Roach Baits
	Real Kill Ant & Roach Killer Time Release Capsules (+ allethrin)
	Real Kill Wasp & Hornet Killer II (+ allethrin)
	Spectracide Ant & Roach Killer (+ allethrin)
	Victory Flea & Tick Fogger (+ allethrin)
cyfluthrin	Raid Liquid Control Tip Ant & Roach Killer
	Raid Max Fogger (+ pyrethrin)
	Raid Max Roach & Ant Killer (+ pyrethrin)
cypermethrin	Enforcer Overnite Pest Control
	Vikor Dual Action Home and Patio Spray (+ pyrethrin)
diazinon	Diazinon
	Ferti-lome Stinger Wasp & Hornet Spray
	Ferti-lome Bug Blaster RTU Indoor/Outdoor Insect Spray
	Ferti-lome Time Release Home & Garden Insect Control
	Hi-Yield Ant Killer Granules
	Ortho Hi-Power Ant, Roach & Spider Spray Formula II (+ pyrethrin)
dichlorvos	Bio-Strip Pest Strip
d-phenothrin	Bengal Roach & Ant Spray
	Black Leaf Flying & Crawling Insect Killer (+ tetramethrin)
	Combat Flying Insect Killer (+ tetramethrin)
	Enforcer Flea Killer for Carpets
	Enforcer Flying Insect Killer (+ tetramethrin)
	Enforcer Overnite Roach Spray
	Enforcer Wasp & Yellowjacket Foam (+ tetramethrin)
	Hi-Yield Roach Blaster
	K-Rid House & Garden Bug Killer (+ tetramethrin)
	K-Rid Flying Insect Killer (+ tetramethrin)
	K-Rid Wasp & Hornet Killer (+ allethrin)
	Meijer Ant Killer Spray (+ tetramethrin)

NOTE: This table lists the trade names of many of the ready-to-use (RTU) household insecticides. Insecticides should be selected by the insecticide listed in the heading under "common name," not those in parentheses in this table. The insecticides listed in parentheses will add some control to the situation, but the one in the heading will be as effective or more effective in controlling the pest. Some products may be available under trade names that are not listed above. Trade names are capitalized; common names are not.

Table 8. Common and Trade Names of Ready-to-Use Household Insecticides (cont.)

Common name	Trade name
d-phenothrin (cont.)	Meijer Wasp & Hornet Killer (+ tetramethrin) Ortho Ant-Stop Ant Killer Spray (+ tetramethrin) Ortho Flea-B-Gon Flea Killer Formula II (+ tetramethrin) Ortho Flying & Crawling Insect Killer Formula III (+ d-trans allethrin) Ortho Home & Garden Insect Killer Formula II (+ tetramethrin) Ortho Household Insect Killer Formula II (+ tetramethrin) Raid Flying Insect Killer (+ allethrin) Raid Roach & Flea Fogger (+ tetramethrin, pyrethrins) Red Circle Powerhouse Roach & Pest Exterminator Safer Wasp & Hornet Killer
fenvalerate	Black Flag Room Fogger
hydramethylnon	Combat Ant Killing System Combat Roach Control Gel Combat Roach Control System Combat Roach Killing System Combat Superbait
hydroprene	Black Flag Roach Ender (+ permethrin) Raid Max Plus Roach Bait (+ chlorpyrifos)
methoprene	Enforcer Flea Spray (+ permethrin) Enforcer 7 Month Flea Spray (+ permethrin) K-Rid Flea Killer 210 (+ pyrethrin) Ortho Total Flea Control (+ permethrin) Ortho Total Flea Killer (+ permethrin) Ortho Total Flea Killer Spray (+ pyrethrin) Raid Flea Killer Plus (+ tetramethrin, pyrethrin) Raid Flea Killer Plus Fogger (+ pyrethrin) Starbar 210 Day Carpet Spray (+ pyrethrin)
permethrin	Black Flag Roach Ender (+ pyrethrin) Black Leaf Roach, Ant & Spider Killer (+ tetramethrin) Combat Ant & Roach Killer (+ pyrethrin) Combat Room Fogger (+ tetramethrin) Enforcer Four Hour Fogger (+ pyrethrin) Hi-Yield Permethrin 1E Hot Shot Fogger (+ tetramethrin) Meijer Home Insect Fogger (+ pyrethrin) Ortho Hi-Power Indoor Insect Fogger (+ pyrethrin) Raid Ant & Roach Killer (+ pyrethrin) Raid Fumigator Raid Max Fogger (+ pyrethrin) Raid Roach & Flea Fogger (+ pyrethrin)

NOTE: This table lists the trade names of many of the ready-to-use (RTU) household insecticides. Insecticides should be selected by the insecticide listed in the heading under "common name," not those in parentheses in this table. The insecticides listed in parentheses will add some control to the situation, but the one in the heading will be as effective or more effective in controlling the pest. Some products may be available under trade names that are not listed above. Trade names are capitalized; common names are not.

Table 8. Common and Trade Names of Ready-to-Use Household Insecticides (cont.)

Common name	Trade name
permethrin (cont.)	Raid Wasp & Hornet Killer (+ tetramethrin) Raid Yard Guard Outdoor Fogger Formula V (+ allethrin) Spectracide Indoor Fogger (+ tetramethrin)
propoxur	Baygon Black Flag Ant & Roach Killer Black Flag Special City Formula II Roach Killer Black Flag Wasp & Hornet Killer Black Leaf Ant Traps Green Thumb Ant Traps Green Thumb Wasp & Hornet Killer K-Rid Wasp & Hornet Killer (+ allethrin) Meijer Ant Traps Ortho Ant Killer Bait Ortho Earwig, Roach & Sowbug Bait Ortho Hornet & Wasp Killer Raid Ant & Roach Killer Raid Wasp & Hornet Killer (+ tetramethrin) Red Circle Foam Guard Wasp & Hornet Killer (+ allethrin)
pyrethrin	Ortho Pet Flea & Tick Spray Natural Guard Dual-Action Crawling Insect Control (+ diatomaceous earth) Natural Guard Natural Insect Spray Raid House & Garden Insect Spray
resmethrin	Black Leaf Fly & Mosquito Spray (+ allethrin, cinerin) Burgess Bug Killer Enforcer Wasp & Hornet Killer Green Thumb Flying Insect Killer (+ d-trans allethrin) Green Thumb Patio Fogger Green Thumb Roach, Ant & Spider Killer Ortho Outdoor Insect Fogger Raid Multibug Killer (+ d-trans allethrin)
sulfluramid	Enforcer Battle Stations for Roaches Raid Ant Baits Plus Raid Max Roach Bait
tetramethrin	Hi-Yield Indoor Fogger Hot Shot K-Rid Flying Insect Killer K-Rid House & Garden Bug Killer (+ pyrethrin) Raid Flea Killer (+ pyrethrin) Raid Flying Insect Killer (+ allethrin) Raid Fogger II (+ pyrethrin)

NOTE: This table lists the trade names of many of the ready-to-use (RTU) household insecticides. Insecticides should be selected by the insecticide listed in the heading under "common name," not those in parentheses in this table. The insecticides listed in parentheses will add some control to the situation, but the one in the heading will be as effective or more effective in controlling the pest. Some products may be available under trade names that are not listed above. Trade names are capitalized; common names are not.

Table 8. Common and Trade Names of Ready-to-Use Household Insecticides (cont.)

Common name	Trade name
tetramethrin (cont.)	Raid House & Garden Bug Killer (+ pyrethrin) Raid House & Garden Formula II (+ pyrethrin) Raid Roach & Flea Fogger (+ pyrethrin)
tralomethrin	Hot Shot Rid-a-Bug Home Insect Killer Hot Shot Roach & Ant Killer Spectracide Home Insect Control

NOTE: This table lists the trade names of many of the ready-to-use (RTU) household insecticides. Insecticides should be selected by the insecticide listed in the heading under "common name," not those in parentheses in this table. The insecticides listed in parentheses will add some control to the situation, but the one in the heading will be as effective or more effective in controlling the pest. Some products may be available under trade names that are not listed above. Trade names are capitalized; common names are not.

Authors

P. Nixon and **J. Lloyd**
*Department of Natural Resources and Environmental Sciences
and Illinois Natural History Survey*

"Managing Pests of Pets" written by

C. Jones and **A. Paul**
Department of Veterinary Pathology

CHAPTER SIX

Managing Pests in Home Fruit Plantings

1 *Fragaria & Fraga.*
Red Strawberries.

Pest management is necessary to grow top-quality fruit. Diseases, insects, mites, birds, and rodents attack all types of fruits grown in home plantings.

Proper planting, pruning, fertilizing, and fruit-thinning are important pest-control practices. Check with your local Extension office or the University of Illinois, ACES/ITCS Product Sales and Distribution, 1401 S. Maryland Dr., Urbana, IL 61801, for publications on these topics.

Production Tips

Prune fruit trees annually to keep them short and open. Well-pruned trees are less susceptible to several diseases, are easier to spray, and dry more quickly. Destroy all prunings, particularly dead and diseased branches.

Keep the grass under and around trees mowed to reduce mouse damage to trunks.

Pick up and destroy fallen fruit. In the fall, collect all fallen leaves and fruit. Then burn, compost, or bury them.

Disease-Resistant Apple Trees

Apple trees vary greatly in their susceptibility to various apple diseases. Researchers and apple breeders have developed apple cultivars with disease resistance to apple scab, powdery mildew, cedar apple rust, and fire blight. Homeowners can greatly reduce the number of sprays necessary to produce quality apples by planting disease-resistant trees. Red Delicious (with its bud sports), Golden Delicious, McIntosh, Jonathan, and Winesap are very susceptible. Prima, Priscilla, Jonafree, Freedom, Liberty, Dayton, Williams' Pride, GoldRush, Enterprise, Redfree, and Pristine are new apple varieties that are highly resistant or immune to the scab fungus.

See the notes under the spray schedule for each fruit species for specific production practices.

Spraying Tips

Good spray coverage is essential for adequate pest control. Thoroughly wet the lower and upper surfaces of leaves, the fruit, the limbs, and the trunk. Because coverage is more difficult in the upper portions of the tree, direct two-thirds of the spray into the top of the tree. Spray until the leaves begin to drip.

If the leaves or fruit are waxy, spray may remain in droplets instead of spreading evenly. After filling the sprayer, add one teaspoon of liquid household detergent per gallon of spray to help spread the spray.

If damage-free fruit is your goal, do not skip sprays. Depending on the crop, sprays may be needed on a 7- to 14-day schedule.

Always heed the following suggestions:

1. Never put herbicides (weed killers) in sprayers that will be used for insect and disease control.

2. For optimal disease control, spray before rains, and allow sufficient time for the spray to dry. Most disease-causing organisms infect wet plants.

3. Prepare just enough spray mix for each application. Never save spray mix for later use.

4. Stir or shake the spray mixture frequently so that the pesticides do not settle out.

5. Rinse the sprayer immediately when you finish. Do not wait until the next day; such a delay may result in a clogged sprayer.

6. During bloom, fungicide sprays may be applied as recommended, but do not use insecticides. Honey bees and other pollinating insects are essential for many kinds of fruit to develop. If insecticides are applied during bloom, these helpful insects are killed and plants produce little or no fruit.

Tank Mix and Multipurpose Mix

Wettable powders (WP) are preferred over emulsifiable concentrates (EC) because liquid concentrates are more likely to injure leaves and fruit.

Unless wettable powders are thoroughly dispersed in water, they clog the spray nozzle. To mix sprays in compressed-air and similar types of sprayers without agitators, measure the pesticide, place it in the tank, and then use a hose to fill the sprayer. Use the hose nozzle to thoroughly mix the spray as the tank is filled. While spraying, shake the tank frequently to keep the pesticide suspended.

Another mixing method is to place the pesticide in a small can or jar, add a small amount of water, and stir into a smooth, thin slurry. The slurry is then washed into the spray tank, and the tank filled to the desired level.

For a sprayer equipped with a mechanical agitator, fill the tank one-third full with water, start the engine and the agitator, add the pesticide, and then finish filling the sprayer.

Using a ready-to-use multipurpose mix (Table 1) is sometimes more convenient than mixing separate pesticides. Many multipurpose fruit spray mixes are available. These mixes usually contain one or two insecticides, one or two fungicides, and rarely a miticide. A widely sold multipurpose fruit spray contains methoxychlor, malathion, and captan. The individual components also may be purchased in 1- to 5-pound packages and mixed as needed.

Imidan or diazinon may be substituted for the combination of malathion and methoxychlor for most fruit crops. However, imidan is labeled only for tree fruits and grapes; and diazinon is not to be used on brambles. Alternative insecticides that are approved for use on fruits in organic production and are available to

Table 1. Multipurpose Spray Mix

Materials	Amount of spray mix to add to water to make[a]		
	1 gallon	5 gallons	10 gallons
	tbsp	*cup(s)*	*cup(s)*
methoxychlor	2	1	2
plus malathion, 25%WP	2	¾	1½
plus captan, 50%WP	1½	¾	1¼

[a]These amounts are only estimates derived from the labels.

homeowners include azadirachtin (trade names Align, Azatin, Neem, and Neemix), soap sprays (M-Pede and Safer Insecticidal Soap), and *Bacillus thuringiensis* vars. *kurstaki* and *aizawai* (Dipel and many other trade names).

Azadirachtin is a broad-spectrum insecticide that may be substituted for any insecticide in Table 2, although it may not be as effective against aphids, mites, and immature stages of a few other pests. Products that contain *Bacillus thuringiensis (Bt)* are effective against foliage-eating caterpillars. Other pesticides not mentioned in this chapter also are registered for use on certain fruits and may be substituted in the schedules. Always follow label directions when using such products.

The initial investment for a multipurpose spray is considerably less than buying each material individually; but, over a period of years, the cost for a multipurpose spray usually is greater for three reasons. First, the cost per pound of pesticide usually is greater. Second, not all ingredients in the multipurpose spray are needed for each application. And third, for some fruits, less costly materials are just as effective. Mixing the separate chemicals allows variations in the mixture to suit the conditions and the plant being sprayed.

Most spray chemicals retain their effectiveness for three or more years if kept dry. Store all pesticides in their original containers in a locked cabinet, preferably in a garage or shed—not inside the home.

Insecticides, miticides, and fungicides are sold under a number of trade

Table 2. Common and Trade Names of Pesticides

Common name	Trade name
Insecticides and miticides	
carbaryl	Sevin, 50WP
diazinon	Diazinon, 50WP
malathion	Malathion, 25WP and 57EC
methoxychlor	Methoxychlor, 50WP
Fungicides	
benomyl	Benlate, 50WP
captan	Captan, 50WP
wettable sulfur	Many names are used.

(or product) names. To avoid confusion, both common (or generic) and trade names are used in Table 2. The common name of the pesticide is always shown on the label as the active ingredient.

A common problem in spraying is knowing how much spray mixture to apply. Table 3 provides a guide based on tree height, width (spread), and growth stage.

Table 3. Approximate Amount of Spray Required for Fruit Trees of Various Sizes

Height in feet	Spread in feet	Gallons per tree per application[a]
4	3	up to ½
5 to 8	3 to 6	¼ to 1
8 to 10	4 to 8	½ to 2
10 to 15	8 to 15	1 to 3
15 to 20	15 to 25	2 to 6

[a]Use the larger amount for trees in full foliage.

Spray Schedules

The amounts given in the following spray schedules (Tables 4 to 11) are in level teaspoons (tsp), level tablespoons (tbsp), and level or partial cups. One level cup equals 16 tablespoons. The suggested amounts are adequate for control. Do not use more pesticide than labels instruct. Excessive concentrations or amounts may injure foliage or fruit. Insufficient concentrations may fail to control pests.

Preventing Mouse Damage

Mice are serious pests of apple and, sometimes, other fruit trees. They eat bark from the trunk near and below the groundline and from the roots. Young and old trees can be damaged. Mouse injury is usually more serious in late fall, winter, and early spring—when other food is scarce.

Predators such as cats, hawks, owls, and foxes can greatly reduce the mouse population if protective cover is eliminated. Mow the grass closely, especially under the trees, and kill all grass and weeds within one foot of the trunk.

Mulches are advantageous for fruit trees, but they harbor mice. In autumn, remove mulch to leave one foot of bare ground around each tree.

Mouse traps and poisons may be used. A repellent on the trunk near the groundline also can help protect trees from mouse damage. Use a commercially prepared rabbit repellent that contains thiram. Spray or paint the lower trunk in late November and again in February.

A gravel collar around the tree trunk discourages mice and helps control grass and weeds. The collar should be made of "pea gravel" and be 6 to 8 inches deep and about 2 feet in diameter. The gravel should remain loose to prevent damage to the trunk.

Prairie Vole

Preventing Rabbit Damage

In fall, winter, and early spring—when food is more scarce—rabbits feed on the bark of the trunk and lower limbs of fruit trees. They also eat the bark from blackberry and raspberry bushes and the buds on young blueberry plants. Rabbits seldom cause much damage to older fruit trees or blueberry plants.

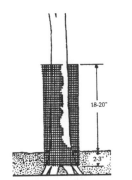

Wire Mesh Around Tree Trunk

Mechanical barriers prevent rabbit damage unless deep snows occur. For young trees, use a circular metal guard (18 inches tall and 6 inches in diameter) made from an 18-inch square of hardware cloth. Or wrap the trunk and lower branches with several layers of newspaper in early November, and remove the papers in April.

The most practical mechanical barrier for protecting blackberry, raspberry, and young blueberry plants is a chicken-wire fence 18 to 21 inches tall.

Commercially prepared repellents that contain thiram are effective. In October or November, paint or spray the parts of plants that need protection from rabbits.

Preventing Bird Damage

Netting over Fruit Tree

Birds are especially destructive pests of blueberries and cherries, and they frequently damage other fruits. Because it is illegal to kill songbirds, covering plants with netting prior to fruit ripening is the only practical method of reducing losses. Picking fruit promptly is suggested.

Aluminum pie pans and other reflecting objects (scare eyes, owl decoys, rubber snakes) hung in fruit plants provide some protection, but birds become accustomed to their presence.

Tips for Handling Pesticides

All pesticides should be handled with care. The pesticides suggested in this chapter are relatively low in toxicity, but careless use can result in injury or illness. Here are some guidelines:

◆ Read and follow all label directions.

◆ Keep pesticides in their original containers; and lock them away from children, pets, food, and feeds.

◆ Avoid getting spray materials and spray on the skin. If this happens, wash the area with soap and water *immediately.*

◆ Mix sprays in a well-ventilated area to avoid breathing spray dust and fumes.

◆ Wear rubber gloves, goggles, a cap, a long-sleeved shirt, and full-length pants when spraying. Avoid breathing the dust or spray.

◆ Don't smoke or eat while spraying or handling pesticides.

◆ Don't spray from under the tree canopy.

◆ Wash thoroughly with soap and water when you finish applying any pesticide. Also launder clothing immediately after spraying.

◆ Don't allow spray to drift onto other plants, birdbaths, fishponds, or water supplies.

◆ Thoroughly rinse and then dispose of containers in a manner that prevents their reuse.

Additional Information

Many references that are available in bookstores and at garden supply stores provide additional information on pests of fruit plants. Among them, *The Backyard Orchardist* by Stello Otto, Ottographics, Maple City, MI, ISBN 0-9634520-3-7, is especially useful.

Table 4. Spray Schedule for Apples, Crabapples, Pears, and Quinces

Mix no.	Time to apply	Spray material	Per 1 gal	Per 10 gal	Remarks
			tbsp	*cup(s)*	
1	Dormant; *before* buds swell, *not later*	Plant spray oil	5	3	Spray only when the temperature will not drop to freezing for 24 hours.
2	When green tissue is ½ inch out of bud and *again* when flower buds show color	Captan *plus* Diazinon *or* multipurpose fruit spray *plus* sulfur (if needed)	1½ 1 1	1 ¾ ¾	Add 5 tablespoons of wettable sulfur per gallon or 1 *teaspoon* of Benlate if powdery mildew is a problem on apples.
3	When three-fourths of the petals have fallen	Same as no. 2 mix	Same as no. 2 mix		For powdery mildew, see remark above. If bees are still coming to flowers, delay application or do not include an insecticide in the spray mix.
4	7 to 10 days after no. 3 mix	Same as no. 2 mix	Same as no. 2 mix		For powdery mildew, see remark above. Insecticide applications at this time and again in about 2 weeks are especially important to prevent codling moth larvae from entering fruit.
5	Continue sprays at 7- to 10-day intervals until July 1.	Same as no. 2 mix	Same as no. 2 mix		For powdery mildew, see remark above.
6	Continue sprays at 10- to 14-day intervals until 2 weeks before harvest.	Same as no. 2 mix	Same as no. 2 mix		For powdery mildew, see remark above.

NOTE: Apply dormant sprays only when the temperature is above freezing and before buds show green tips. Borers that attack apple and pear trees are controlled by the spray schedule above if the trunk is thoroughly sprayed. If borers have attacked young, nonbearing trees, spray the trunks every 2 weeks during June and July with a multipurpose fruit spray. For apple maggot control in the northern half of Illinois and codling moth control throughout the state, continue to apply an insecticide or multipurpose fruit spray every 10 to 14 days through July and August.

Table 5. Spray Schedule for Grapes

Mix no.	Time to apply	Spray material	Per 1 gal	Per 10 gal	Remarks
			tbsp	*cup(s)*	
1	New growth 2 to 4 inches long and again at 10 to 15 inches long	Captan, *plus* Sevin *or* Malathion, 25%WP	1½ 2 2	1½ 1 1	Primarily for control of black rot and flea beetles. Use Sevin or Malathion only if flea beetles are damaging buds or leaves (symptoms are small holes in leaves).
2	Just before bloom	Same as no. 1 mix	Same as no. 1 mix		If powdery mildew has been a problem in previous years, add 1 *teaspoon* of Benlate per gallon of spray mix.
3	Just after bloom (when berries have set)	Captan *plus* Sevin (if needed)	1½ 2	1½ 1	Add Sevin only if insects are a problem.
4	3 weeks after the last spray	Captan	1½	1½	For black rot control.

NOTE: Grapes must be pruned and retied annually. Clean cultivation helps control flea beetles, cutworms, and disease-causing organisms. Select strong, healthy canes of the previous year's growth to produce the following season's crop. After the fruiting canes have been selected, remove excess growth, dried berries, and leaves. Destroy (burn) all prunings. The most important problem is black rot, which appears on the leaves as small, reddish brown to tan-brown spots with dark margins. "Bird's-eye" tan spots on the fruit rapidly enlarge. Berries quickly rot and turn into black, wrinkled mummies that drop early.

Table 6. Spray Schedule for Currants and Gooseberries

Mix no.	Time to apply	Spray material	Per 1 gal	Per 10 gal	Remarks
1	Dormant (before growth starts)	Plant spray oil	5 tbsp	3 cups	For control of scale insects and aphids.
2	When leaf tips show green	Malathion, 57%EC, *plus* wettable sulfur	2 tsp 3 tbsp	7 tbsp 2 cups	Use Malathion if aphids infest new growth or if foliage-eating insects are causing damage.
3	Full foliage	Malathion, 57%EC	2 tsp	7 tbsp	Same as for no. 2 mix. Use Malathion only if aphids or scales are a problem.

NOTE: Prune out and destroy infested or diseased plant parts.

Table 7. Spray Schedule for Blueberries

Time to apply	Spray material	Per 1 gal	Per 10 gal	Remarks
		tbsp	*cup(s)*	
As buds break open and until three-fourths of the blossoms have dropped	Benlate	½	½	Application of insecticides is rarely necessary in blueberries in Illinois. If pest problems appear, apply Malathion or Sevin according to label directions at 10-day to 2-week intervals.

NOTE: Pruning out old canes and removing small, weak, diseased wood with hand shears reduces insect, mite, and disease problems. All prunings should be removed and disposed of, preferably by burning. Heavy nitrogen fertilization increases the chances for more severe disease problems.

Table 8. Spray Schedule for Peaches, Nectarines, Apricots, and Plums

Mix no.	Time to apply	Spray material	Per 1 gal	Per 10 gal	Remarks
			tbsp	*cup(s)*	
1	Dormant; *early spring, before* buds swell, *not later*	Captan *or* multipurpose fruit spray	1½	1½	This is the *only* spray that controls peach leaf curl and plum pockets.
2	When fruit buds show color (or turn pink)	Captan *or* Benlate[a]	1½ ½	1½ ½	Do *not* use insecticides during bloom; pollinating insects will be killed.
3	During bloom	Captan *or* Benlate[a]	1½ ½	1½ ½	Important for blossom blight control.
4	When husks begin to split and pull away from the base of the fruit	Wettable sulfur *plus* Captan *plus* Diazinon OR multipurpose fruit spray *plus* sulfur	3 1½ 1	2 1½ ¾	Sulfur is needed for scab control on peaches and may be added to a multipurpose fruit spray.
5	7 to 10 days after no. 4	Same as no. 4 mix			
6	Continue sprays at 10- to 14-day intervals until 4 weeks before harvest.	Same as no. 4 mix			
7	10 to 14 days after no. 6	Malathion, 25% WP, *plus* Captan	1½ 2	1 2	Within 1 week of harvest, spray Captan alone to control brown rot.

NOTE: For special borer sprays for peaches, nectarines, cherries, plums, and apricots, spray or paint only the trunk and lower limbs with 3 tablespoons of Sevin per gallon of water about June 15, July 15, and August 15.
[a]Benlate should be alternated or combined with Captan in the spray schedule to prevent the occurrence of Benlate-tolerant strains of fungi. *Never* use Benlate alone in repeated spray applications.

Table 9. Spray Schedule for Cherries

Mix no.	Time to apply	Spray material	Per 1 gal	Per 10 gal	Remarks
			tbsp	*cup(s)*	
1	When husks begin to split and pull away from the base of the fruit	Captan	1½	1	This spray is important in controlling brown rot.
		plus Malathion, 25%WP,	1½	1	
		or Diazinon,	1	¾	
		OR			
		multipurpose fruit spray			
2	7 to 10 days after no. 1 mix	Same as no. 1 mix			
3	Just after fruit is harvested and again 2 to 3 weeks later	Captan	2	1½	This spray is very important to control leaf spot and to prevent leaves from dropping prematurely.

NOTE: For special borer sprays for cherries, see the schedule for peaches. Benlate gives outstanding control of cherry leaf spot and, if available, is recommended as a replacement for Captan.

Table 10. Spray Schedule for Strawberries

Mix no.	Time to apply	Spray material	Per 1 gal	Per 10 gal	Remarks
			tbsp	*cup(s)*	
1	Early bloom	Multipurpose fruit spray,	1½	1½	Apply at the appearance of the first blossoms to control gray mold.
		plus Captan	1	½	
		or Benlate[a]			
2	Cover sprays 7 to 10 days after no. 1 mix; repeat every 7 to 10 days until harvest.	Captan *or* Benlate[a]	½	½	Apply Captan or Benlate[a] from bloom through harvest at weekly intervals; use Benlate if powdery mildew develops. During full bloom, to avoid killing bees, do not use a multipurpose spray that contains an insecticide.
3	Postharvest sprays	Multipurpose fruit spray			Apply one or more times after renovation to protect new foliage.

NOTE: To reduce insect and disease problems of strawberries:
1. Renovate beds annually, immediately after harvest.
2. Use certified, virus-free plants for new plantings. Plan a good aphid-control program during spring and summer to reduce the chance of contaminating your virus-free plantings. Malathion is recommended against aphids.
3. Practice crop rotation. Because of the possibility that Verticillium wilt may develop, avoid planting strawberries within 3 years of planting tomatoes, peppers, potatoes, eggplant, melons, or roses. Strawberry varieties most resistant to Verticillium wilt include Allstar, Catskill, Delite, Earliglow, Guardian, Redchief, Sunrise, Surecrop, Tennessee Beauty, Tribute, and Tristar.
4. Plant red stele–resistant varieties; this is the *only* control for this disease. Planting in light, well-drained soil is recommended. The following strawberry varieties are resistant to red stele root rot (the number in parentheses is the number of races of the fungus to which the variety is resistant): Allstar (2), Darrow (5), Delite (5), Earliglow (5), Guardian (5), Midway (2), Redchief (5), Sunrise (5), Surecrop (5), Tribute (2), and Tristar (2).
5. Avoid white grubs. Do not plant strawberries on sod land until it has been under cultivation at least 2 years. If grub damage is present, apply diazinon as a postharvest treatment.
6. If slugs are a problem, apply metaldehyde bait according to label directions.
[a]Benlate should be alternated or combined with Captan in the spray schedule to prevent the occurrence of Benlate-tolerant strains of fungi.

Table 11. Spray Schedule for Brambles (Blackberries and Raspberries)

Mix no.	Time to apply	Spray material	Per 1 gal	Per 10 gal	Remarks
1	Delayed dormant (before leaflets are ⅜-inch long)	Liquid lime–sulfur	1½ cups	1 gal	For control of mites, scale insects, anthracnose, and spur blight
2	Cover sprays (when new canes are 6 to 8 inches tall, just before bloom, and immediately after bloom)	Sevin *or* Malathion, 25%WP	2 tbsp 2 tbsp	1 cup 1 cup	
3	Special sprays	Malathion, 25%WP	2 tbsp	1 cup	Apply as fruit begins to color for controling picnic beetles.

NOTE: To reduce insect and disease problems of brambles:
1. Remove and dispose of insect-infested, diseased, and old fruiting canes immediately after harvest. Thin out all weak, short, spindly, and injured canes. Clean cultivation helps control fruit worms.
2. Remove all nearby wild brambles and neglected plantings.
3. Keep fruit plantings and surrounding areas free of weeds.
4. Use certified, virus-free plants when starting a new planting. Select adapted, disease-resistant varieties.
5. All plants infected with orange rust, crown gall, and viruses must be dug out and removed from the planting when first noticed.
6. See spray schedule for strawberries for note on Verticillium wilt control.

Table 12. Relative Effectiveness of Fungicides Against Specific Diseases of Various Fruit Crops

Fruits and diseases	Benomyl (Benlate)	Captan	Wettable sulfur
Apple			
Scab	xxx	xx	x
Cedar rusts	0	0	0
Powdery mildew	xxx	0	xxx
Sooty blotch, flyspeck	xxx	xx	x
Stone fruits			
Brown rot of peach, plum, cherry, apricots	xxx	xx	x
Peach scab	xxx	xx	xxx
Strawberry			
Leaf spots and blights	xxx	xx	–
Gray mold	xxx	xx	–
Grape			
Black rot	x	xx	0
Downy mildew	0	xxx	0
Powdery mildew	xxx	0	xxx
Raspberry			
Fruit rot, anthracnose, spur blight, cane blight	xxx	xx	–

NOTE: xxx = very good, xx = good, x = fair, 0 = not effective, and – = not labeled for this use.

Authors

S. Ries
Department of Crop Sciences

R. Weinzierl
*Department of Crop Sciences
and the Illinois Natural History Survey*

Proper Use of Pesticides

I *Pyrethrum officinarum.*
Pellitorie of Spaine.

Once you have identified a pest and determined that its numbers are high enough to cause damage, efforts are usually warranted. Once chemical control options have been considered, pesticides may be used as part of your integrated pest management plan. The following information should be useful to you in using pesticides correctly and safely. Always read and follow the directions on the pesticide's label.

Understanding Pesticides
What exactly are pesticides?

The word *pesticide* is a general term used to describe any substance that is used to kill a pest or to prevent or reduce the damage caused by a pest.

Most pesticides fall into certain categories.

Each category targets certain types of pests. It is important that you use the correct product for the job.

◆ Disinfectants (kill bacteria, mold, and mildew)
 Bleach
 Ammonia
 Disinfectant aerosols
 Kitchen and bathroom cleaners
 Tub and tile cleaners
 Pool and spa cleaners

◆ Insecticides (kill or repel insects, ticks, and mites)
 Garden dusts
 Soap sprays
 Mosquito repellents, bug sprays
 Ant and roach baits
 Flea shampoos, flea and tick collars
 Moth balls

◆ Herbicides (kill weeds or unwanted plants)
 Weed killers
 Weed-and-feed lawn care products
 Cut-stump treatments

◆ Fungicides (kill mold, mildew, and other fungi)
Rose and flower sprays
Treated seeds
Paint additives to prevent mildew growth

◆ Rodenticides (kill rodents such as mice and rats)
Mouse and rat bait stations
Wood preservatives(protect wood from insects and fungi)
Pressure-treated wood

How can I identify a pesticide?

All pesticides can be identified by the presence of an Environmental Protectio Agency (EPA) registration number (for example, EPA Reg. No. 1234-567). By law, this number must be located on the product container or label of any pesticide. Before any product may be sold or used as a pesticide, the EPA reviews all appropriate data to ensure the product causes no undue risk to people or the environment.

Are pesticides dangerous?

Yes, they can be. That is why anyone using pesticides must read and follow the instructions provided on the product container or label. It's not only smart, it's the law! The danger of any product is evaluated not only by its toxicity, but also by the degree of your exposure to the product. As Paracelsus, the "father" of modern toxicology, put it, "the dose makes the poison."

Pesticides are not the only poisons: Plants, fungi, and bacteria produce some of the most toxic compounds known. Nature is the "best" chemist.

Are pesticides important?

As you read at the start of this paper, pesticides are valuable to us in many ways. They help us to control or reduce hundreds of pests in and around our home, as well as in agricultural and commercial settings. Others help to maintain our health; disinfectants are used to cleanse kitchens and bathrooms, and repellents are used to ward off nuisance insects and ticks that can carry disease.

Are pesticides necessary?

Sometimes pesticides are necessary, but not in every situation. Oftentimes a good understanding of the pest, and the damage it is capable of, may allow us to prevent problems or decide not to control the pest at all. Nonchemical control methods such as handpicking, cleaning up garbage or food scraps, and proper plant care can often reduce or eliminate pest problems.

Understanding Pesticide Labels

By law, pesticide labels must contain certain kinds of information. Pesticide applicators have the legal responsibility to read, understand, and follow the label directions. Quite often, pesticide applicators fail to take the time to read or follow the specified safety precautions that the label provides. The following label example illustrates the safety sections of a label. To protect yourself and the environment, read the label—it's the law!

As you can see, the label provides you with a great deal of valuable information. Become familiar with the labels of the products that you use before you really need to.

Trade name of product (Cygon)

CYGON
Garden Spray

- Kills Damaging Insects on Trees, Shrubs, Flowers and Vegetables.
- See Right Side of this Panel for a List of Insects Killed.

Common name of product (Dimethoate)

ACTIVE INGREDIENTS:
Dimethoate (0, 0-dimethyl S-[(N-methylcarbamoyl) methyl] phosphorodithioate)* 12.00%
INERT INGREDIENTS:* 88.00%
* Contains 51.41% Xylene

Keep out of reach of children
WARNING
See back panel for additional precautionary statements
For Homeowner Use Only.

What is the relative safety of this pesticide?

In order of low to high toxicity, three signal levels are used

—Caution
—Warning
—Danger–Poison

Proper storage and disposal of product

STORAGE: Store in original container and place in a locked storage area.
DISPOSAL: Do not reuse container. Wrap and put in trash.

PRECAUTIONARY STATEMENTS
HAZARDOUS TO HUMANS AND DOMESTIC ANIMALS

Precautions to take during and after use

WARNING: Harmful or fatal if swallowed, inhaled or absorbed through the skin. Avoid breathing of vapors or spray mist. Avoid contact with skin, eyes and clothing. Wash thoroughly after handling and before eating or smoking. Do not contaminate feed or food stuffs. Keep children and pets off treated areas until treated surfaces have dried completely. Food utensils such as teaspoons and measuring cups should not be used for food purposes after use with insecticides.

PHYSICAL AND CHEMICAL HAZARDS
DO NOT USE, POUR, SPILL OR STORE NEAR HEAT OR OPEN FLAME.
PRECAUTIONARY STATEMENTS

What to do in case of a medical emergency

IF SWALLOWED - Call physician or Poison Control Center immediately. Drink 1 or 2 glasses of water and induce vomiting by touching back of throat with finger. Do not induce vomiting or give anything by mouth to an unconscious person.

IF INHALED - Remove victim to fresh air. Apply artificial respiration if indicated.

IF ON SKIN - Remove contaminated clothing and wash affected areas with soap and water.

IF IN EYES - Flush eyes with plenty of water for at least 15 minutes. Get medical attention.

NOTE TO PHYSICIAN - This product may cause cholinesterase inhibition. Atropine is antidotal. 2-PAM may be effective as an adjunct to atropine.

Are there any special environmental considerations (that is, fish, birds, bees, groundwater contamination) that you should be aware of when using this pesticide?

ENVIRONMENTAL HAZARDS

This product is toxic to fish, birds, and other wildlife. Birds feeding on treated areas may be killed. Do not apply directly to lakes, streams, or ponds. Do not apply when weather conditions favor drift from treated areas. Do not contaminate water by cleaning of equipment or disposal of wastes. Apply the product only as specified on this label. This product is highly toxic to bees exposed to direct treatment or residues on plants. Protective information may be obtained from your Cooperative Agricultural Extension Service.

What do you need to wear during application?

THE FOLLOWING PROTECTIVE CLOTHING MUST BE WORN DURING APPLICATION:
a. Impermeable gloves (for example, rubber or plastic covered reinforced gloves).
b. Boots or boot covers.
c. Long-sleeved shirt and long pants.
d. Wide-brimmed hat.

CYGON*, is a registered trademark of American Cyanamid Co. Buyer assumes all risks of use, storage, and handling of this material not in strict accordance with directions given herewith.

Distributed by American Brand Chemical Co.   Bonham, Texas 75418
EPA Est. No. 7401-TX-1   EPA Reg. No. 7401-338-7679
30M-12-32J   Net Contents One Pint

Environmental Protection Agency (EPA) registration number

What are the legal procedures and uses for this product?

DIRECTIONS FOR USE

It is a violation of Federal law to use this product in a manner inconsistent with its labeling.

AMERICAN BRAND CYGON GARDEN SPRAY is effective in killing insects on trees, shrubs, flowers, and vegetables.

To apply - ... SEE OFFICIAL LABEL

Pesticide Safety and Poisoning Symptoms
How Do Pesticides Enter the Body?

Oral exposure: From the intake or absorption of a pesticide through the mouth.

Inhalation exposure: From breathing in pesticide vapors, dust, or spray particles.

Dermal exposure: From the absorption of a pesticide into the skin.

Did you know?

◆ Deaths from occupational exposure to pesticides are unusual.

◆ Children under 10 years of age represent half the accidental deaths by pesticides.

◆ Nearly all pesticide deaths are caused by eating or drinking the product.

◆ About 90 percent of the exposure that a pesticide user receives is dermal.
  Thoughtfulness and use of appropriate clothing can reduce pesticide exposure.

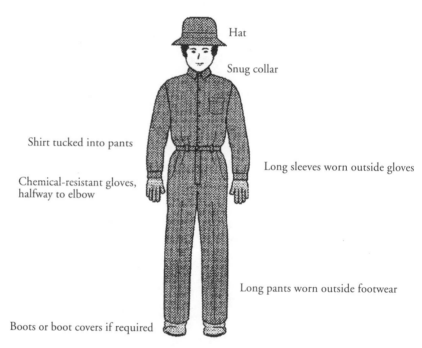

Hat

Snug collar

Shirt tucked into pants

Chemical-resistant gloves,
halfway to elbow

Long sleeves worn outside gloves

Long pants worn outside footwear

Boots or boot covers if required

An appropriately clothed pesticide user

Tips for Safe and Knowledgeable Pesticide Use

◆ Wear all protective clothing and equipment listed on the pesticide
  label, such as long-sleeved shirt and long pants, chemical-resistant gloves and
  boots, eyeware, etc.

◆ Avoid wearing soft contact lenses when working with pesticides. Soft contact
  lenses may absorb pesticide vapors from the air and hold them against your eyes.

◆ Use all pesticides in well-ventilated areas to avoid inhaling fumes.

◆ Do not eat, drink, or use tobacco when working with pesticides because
  trace amounts of chemicals can be transferred from hand to mouth.

◆ Wash your hands thoroughly with soap and water after handling pesticides and before using the toilet or eating.

◆ Always avoid unnecessary exposure to pesticides. Be especially careful to keep children, pregnant women, sensitive individuals, and pets away from areas where pesticides are being or have recently been applied.

◆ Don't spray on a windy day when spray could drift onto you, your neighbors, or your neighbor's yard.

◆ Examine the area to be treated and its surroundings. Are there plants or animals that could be harmed by the pesticide? Don't spray if you cannot guarantee they will not be injured. You are responsible for any damage that occurs.

◆ Store pesticides out of children's reach (preferably in a locked storage area). Always store pesticides in their original containers along with their labels intact.

Symptoms Associated with Pesticide Poisoning

Early symptoms include fatigue, headache, nausea, and dizziness.

Severe symptoms include sweating, stomach cramps, vomiting, diarrhea, and blurred vision.

Pesticide poisoning symptoms may be similar to those caused by heat exhaustion, food poisoning, asthma, or infectious disease. The pattern of symptoms is important in diagnosing the cause.

DO NOT allow yourself or anyone else to become dangerously ill before seeking medical assistance. It is better to be too cautious than too late!

Treatment of Pesticide Poisoning

◆ Contact your local emergency room, hospital, or ambulance.

◆ Read the product label for first-aid instructions.

◆ DO NOT assume that you should induce vomiting; read the label first.

◆ Give the product label and any vomitus to the doctor to aid in diagnosing the problem.

Adapted from PAT Facts, *prepared by Bruce E. Paulsrud, Extension Specialist, Department of Crop Sciences, August 1996.*

Plant Clinic
Specimen Data Form

Plant Clinic
1401 W. St. Mary's Road
Urbana, IL 61802

UNIVERSITY OF ILLINOIS
PLANT CLINIC SPECIMEN DATA FORM

Office Use Only

| Plant Clinic # _____ |
| Date Received _____ |
| County _____ |
| Charge _____ |
| Date Paid _____ Ck # _____ |

Submitter _____

Grower _____

    Commercial_____ Home Grower_____

    County_____

Send response to: Name_____

                  Address_____

                  City_____ State_____ Zip_____

                  Phone# (____)_____

Crop or Plant Name_____ Variety_____

Describe Problems or Symptom/Sketch Distribution:

Symptoms Appeared in Past: Days_____ Weeks_____ Months_____

Describe Conditions Prior to Symptom Development:

      Temperature_____ Rainfall_____ Other _____

Planting History: Crop Two Years Ago_____ Crop One Year Ago _____

Soil Type: _____ pH_____ %Organic Matter _____

Soil Test Information: _____

Type of Nitrogen Application: _____

Chemicals Appled this year:

      Fertilizer_____ Type of Application _____

      Herbicide(s)_____

        Rates _____

        Type of Application _____

Chemicals Applied Last Year _____

Ornamentals:

Approximate Age and Size: _____

Condition of Nearby Species:_____

Where to Get Additional Information

Many times throughout a growing season, you may need to contact someone for specific information to help you make a decision related to pesticides or pest management. The following is a list of addresses and telephone numbers for people and organizations that might be able to provide some assistance.

Environmental Protection Agency, Illinois

A.G. Taylor, Agricultural Adviser
2200 Churchill Rd.
Box 19276
Springfield, IL 62794-9276
(217)782-3397
Emergency Response
(217)782-3637

Hazardous Waste Research and Information Center

David L. Thomas, Director
1 E. Hazelwood Dr.
Champaign, IL 61820
(217)333-8940

Illinois Department of Agriculture

State Fairgrounds
P.O. Box 19281
Springfield, IL 62794-9281
(217)782-2172

Warren Goetsch, Chief
Bureau of Environmental Programs
(217)785-2427

Mark Ringler, Chief
Bureau of Agricultural Products Inspection
(217)782-3817

Illinois Department of Natural Resources

Illinois Natural History Survey
172 Natural Resources Building
607 E. Peabody Dr.
Champaign, IL 61820
(217)333-6880

Illinois Department of Public Health

Fred Riecks
Program Manager/Pesticides
Division of Environmental Health
525 W. Jefferson St.
Springfield, IL 62761
(217)782-5830

Illinois Department of Transportation

Division of Traffic Safety
Commercial Vehicle Safety Section
3215 Executive Park Dr.
P.O. Box 19212
Springfield, IL 62794-9212
(217)785-1181

Illinois Emergency Management Agency

Oran Robinson, Hazardous Materials Officer
110 E. Adams St.
Springfield, IL 62701-9963
(217)782-4694

Emergency Reporting
(800)782-7860 (toll-free in Illinois)

Illinois Fertilizer and Chemical Association

Lloyd Burling, President
P.O. Box 186
St. Anne, IL 60964
(815)427-6644 or (800)892-7122 (toll-free in Illinois)

Victor Thompson, Containment Regulations
  and Systems
3695 S. 6th St.
Springfield, IL 62703
(217)529-0034

USDA/APHIS/Animal Damage Control

Kirk Gustad, District Supervisor
2869 Via Verde Dr.
Springfield, IL 62703-4325
(217)492-4308

University of Illinois, College of Agricultural, Consumer and Environmental Sciences— Academic Units

Agricultural and Consumer Economics

Robert J. Hauser, Head
332 Mumford Hall
1301 W. Gregory Dr.
Urbana 61801

Agricultural Engineering

Loren E. Bode, Head
338 Agricultural Engineering Sciences Building
1304 W. Pennsylvania Ave.

Animal Sciences

Robert A. Easter, Head
116 Animal Sciences Laboratory
1207 W. Gregory Dr.
Urbana 61801

Crop Sciences

Gary H. Heichel, Head
AW-101 Turner Hall
1102 S. Goodwin Ave.
Urbana 61801

Food Science and Human Nutrition

Bruce M. Chassy, Head
260 Bevier Hall
905 S. Goodwin
Urbana 61801

Human and Community Development

Constance H. Shapiro, Head
274 Bevier Hall
905 S. Goodwin Ave.
Urbana 61801

Natural Resources and Environmental Sciences

Gary L. Rolfe, Head
W-503 Turner Hall
1102 S. Goodwin Ave.
Urbana 61801

Nutritional Sciences

John W. Erdman, Jr., Director
451 Bevier Hall
905 S. Goodwin Ave.
Urbana 61801

Veterinary Research and Extension

Victor E. Valli, Head
3505 Veterinary Medicine Basic Sciences Building
2001 S. Lincoln Ave.
Urbana 61801
Paul, Allan, Small Animals

University of Illinois Cooperative Extension Service State Specialists

Agricultural Engineering

Aherin, Robert, Farm Safety
  (217)333-9417
Bode, Loren, Pesticide Application Technology
  (217)333-3570
Funk, Ted, Grain Drying, Stored Grains
  (217)333-9313
Hirschi, Mike, Soil and Water
  (217)333-9410
Siemens, John, Power and Machinery
  (217)333-2854
Wolf, Robert, Pesticide Application Technology
  (217)333-9418

Aquatic and Ornamental

Ferree, Rhonda, Pesticide Applicator Training,
  Weed Control
  (217)244-4397

Crop Sciences

(217)333-4424
Eastburn, Darin, Vegetable Crop Diseases
  (217)333-1845
Edwards, Dale, Nematology
  (217)244-2011
Graffis, Don, Forage Crops
  (217) 333-4424
Gray, Mike, Integrated Pest Management and Field
  Crop Insects
  (217)333-6651
Hager, Aaron, Integrated Pest Management
  (217) 333-4424
Hart, Steve, Weed Science
  (217) 333-4424
Hoeft, Bob, Soil Fertility
  (217) 333-4424
McGlamery, Marshal, Weed Science
  (217) 333-4424

Nafziger, Emerson, Crop Production and Physiology
  (217) 333-4424
Pataky, Nancy, Diseases of Ornamentals;
  Director of Plant Clinic
  (217)333-0519 or (217)333-2478
Paulsrud, Bruce, Pesticide Applicator Training, Plant
  Diseases
  (217)244-9646
Pepper, Gary, Soybean Production
Pike, David, Pesticide Impact Assessment and
  Weed Science
Ries, Steve, Fruit Diseases
  (217)333-1523
Steffey, Kevin, Field Crop Insects, Stored Grain Insects,
  and 4-H Entomology
  (217)333-6652
Weinzierl, Rick, Fruit and Vegetable Insects, Livestock
  Insects
  (217)333-6651

Natural Resources and Environmental Sciences

Bolin, Mike, Forestry
  (217) 333-2778
Giles, Floyd, Ornamental Horticulture
  (217)333-2125
Kindhart, Jeff, Small Fruits and Vegetables
  Dixon Springs Agriculture Center
  Rt. 1
  Simpson 62985
  (618)695-2444
Masiunas, John, Vegetable Crops, Weed Control
  (217)244-4469
Nixon, Phil, Pesticide Applicator Training, Household
  and Ornamental Insects
  (217)333-6650
Schmidt, Jim, Ornamental Horticulture,
  Home Vegetables
  (217)244-5153
Shoemaker, William, Horticulture
  Kane County CES Unit Office
  535 Randall Rd.
  St. Charles 60174
  (708)584-6166
Voigt, Charles, Vegetable Crops
  (217)333-1969
Voigt, Tom, Turfgrass, Weed Control
  (217)333-7847
Williams, Dave, Woody Ornamentals, Weed Control,
  Floriculture
  (217)333-2126

University of Illinois Agricultural Research and Demonstration Centers

Brownstown

Kevin Barber, Superintendent
Rt. 2, Box 36A
Brownstown 62418
(618)427-5239

Dixon Springs

Stephen Ebelhar, Superintendent
Agronomy Division
Rt. 1, Box 256
Simpson 62985
(618)695-2790

Northern

Lyle Paul, Superintendent
Rt. 1, Box 36
Shabbona 60550
(815)824-2029

Northwestern

Eric Adee, Superintendent
321 210th Ave.
Monmouth 61462
(309)734-7459

Orr

Glenn Rains, Superintendent
Box 212
Perry 62362
(217)236-4911

University of Illinois Cooperative Extension Service—Centers

Armour Square

10 W. 35th St., Suite 1600
Chicago 60616
(312)808-9510
(312)808-9169 fax

Champaign

1401D Regency East
Savoy 61874
(217)333-4901
(217)333-4943 fax
Suzanne M. Bissonnette, IPM
David Shiley, Natural Resources Management

Countryside

University of Illinois
6438 Joliet Road
Countryside 60525-4642
(708)352-0109
(708)352-0451 fax
Fredric Miller, IPM
James Schuster, Horticulture (Ornamentals)
Greg Stack, Horticulture (Ornamentals)

Decatur

985 W. Pershing Rd., Suite H4
Decatur 62526
(217)876-9697
(217)876-7995
Dennis Bowman, Crop Systems

DeKalb

155 N. 3rd St., Suite 200
DeKalb 60115
(815)748-5200
(815)748-5231 fax
Ellen Mary Phillips, Crop Systems
William Whiteside, Horticulture (Vegetables)

East Peoria

University of Illinois
727 Sabrina Dr.
East Peoria 61611
(309)694-7501
(309)694-7882 fax
Robert W. Frazee, Natural Resources Management

University of Illinois, Cooperative Extension Service—Centers (cont.)

Edwardsville

University of Illinois
200 University Park Dr.
Edwardsville 62025-3636
(618)692-9434
(618)692-9808 fax
Robert C. Bellm, Crop Systems
Anthony Bratsch, Horticulture (Fruits and Vegetables)
Ronald E. Cornwell, Horticulture (Landscape and Turf)

Effingham

1209 Wenthe Dr.
Effingham 62401-1697
(217)347-5126
(217)347-5150 fax

Freeport

773 W. Lincoln, Suite 403
Freeport 61032
(815)233-3214
(815)233-4511 fax
Jim Morrison, Crop Systems

Grayslake

98 S. U.S. Highway 45
Grayslake 60030-2202
(708)223-3433
(708)223-3499 fax
Bruce Spangenberg, Horticulture (Ornamentals)

Kankakee

1004 W. Lincoln Ave.
Manteno 60950
(815)468-2537
(815)468-3053
Joseph Toman, Jr., IPM

Macomb

480 S. Deere Rd.
Macomb 61455
(309)836-3366
(309)836-2916 fax
Martha Smith, Horticulture (Ornamentals)

Marion

108 Airway Dr.
Marion 62959
(618)997-3919
(618)997-6213 fax
Michael Plumer, Natural Resources Management

Mount Vernon

4112 N. Water Tower Pl.
Mt. Vernon 62864-6295
(618)242-9310
(618)242-9433 fax
Dennis R. Epplin, Crop Systems

Peru

809 21st St.
Peru 61354
(815)223-2540
(815)223-1077 fax
Dale Baird, Crop Systems

Quad Cities

1414 10th St., Suite 2
Silvis 61282
(309)792-2500
(309)792-2602 fax
Dave Feltes, IPM

Rockford

431 S. Phelps, Suite 605
Rockford 61108
(815)397-7714
(815)397-8620 fax
John Church, Natural Resources Management

Springfield

Illinois State Fairground, Bldg. 30 (for UPS mailing)
P.O. Box 8199
Springfield 62791
(217)782-6515
(217)782-8886 fax
William Brink, Crop Systems
George F. Czapar, IPM
David Robson, Horticulture (Ornamentals)

West Rogers Park

2320 W. Peterson Ave., Suite 200
Chicago 60659-5239
(773)761-5099
(773)761-6955 fax

University of Illinois, Cooperative Extension Service—Unit Offices (cont.)

Adams /Brown Unit

330 S. 36th St.
Quincy 62301
(217)223-8380
(217)223-9368 fax (call first)
Michael Roegge, Crops Systems

Mt. Sterling Office (Brown County)
Adams/Brown CES
109 W. North St. (for UPS mailing)
P.O. Box 209
Mt. Sterling, 62353
(217)773-3013

Alexander/Johnson/Massac/
Pulaski/Union Unit

208 E. Main
P.O. Box 158
Vienna 62995
(618)658-5321
(618)658-2028 fax

Anna Office (Union County)
201 Springfield Ave., Suite D
Anna 62906
(618)833-6363
(618)833-6304 fax

Metropolis Office (Massac County)
1438 W. 10th
Metropolis 62960
(618)524-2270
(618)524-3948 fax

Mounds Office (Pulaski/Alexander County)
124 N. Oak St.
Mounds 62964
(618)745-6310
(618)745-6806 fax

Bond County Unit

Lake and Harris Ave.
P.O. Box 129
Greenville 62246
(618)664-3665
(618)664-9277 fax

Boone County Unit

930 W. Locust
Belvidere 61008
(815)544-3710
(815)544-4606 fax

Brown County

See Adams/Brown

Bureau County Unit

850 Thompson St.
Princeton 61356
(815)875-2878
(815)875-2870 fax

Calhoun/Jersey Unit

Box 366 S. Park St.
Hardin 62047
(618)576-2293
(618)576-8013 fax

Jersey Office
1005 E. Shipman Rd.
Jerseyville 62052
(618)498-2913
(618)498-6221 fax

Carroll County

See JoDaviess/Carroll

Cass County

See Schuyler/Cass

Champaign County Unit

1715 W. Springfield
Champaign 61821
(217)333-7672
(217)333-7683 fax
Sandra Mason, Horticulture

Christian County Unit

1120 N. Webster
Taylorville 62568
(217)287-7246
(217)287-7248 fax
Gary A. Letterly, Economic Development/
    Crops/Horticulture

Clark County Unit

RR 2, Box 47
Marshall 62441
(217)826-8631 (also fax)

Clay County

See Effingham/Fayette/Clay

Clinton County Unit

1155 N. Fourth St. (for UPS mailing)
P.O. Box 185
Breese 62230
(618)526-4551
(618)526-4597 fax

University of Illinois, Cooperative Extension Service—Unit Offices (cont.)

Coles County Unit
703 Monroe St.
Charleston 61920
(217)345-7034
(217)345-7035
(217)235-2035 (Mattoon)
(217)348-7940 fax

Cook/Chicago–North Unit
1000 N. Milwaukee
Fourth Floor
Chicago 60622-4005
(773)292-4444
(773)292-4448 fax

Cook/Chicago–South Unit
5106 S. Western Avenue
Chicago 60609-5498
(773)737-1178
(773)776-2148 fax
Ron Wolford, Urban Gardening

Cook/North Suburban Unit
2121 W. Euclid Ave., Room 251
Rolling Meadows 60008
(847)818-2901
(847)818-2904 fax

Cook/South Suburban Unit
17722 Oak Park Ave.
Tinley Park 60477-3936
(708)532-3337
(708)532-8878 fax

Crawford County
301 S. Cross St.
Room 290 Commercium Bldg.
Robinson 62454
(618)546-1549
(618)546-1540 fax

Cumberland County
See Jasper/Cumberland

DeKalb County Unit
1350 W. Prairie Dr.
Sycamore 60178-3166
(815)758-8194
(815)758-8199 fax

DeWitt County Unit
803 W. Leander (for UPS mailing)
P.O. Box 347
Clinton 61727
(217)935-5764
(217)935-8932 fax

Douglas County
See Moultrie/Douglas

DuPage County Unit
310 S. County Farm Rd., Suite B
Wheaton 60187
(708)653-4114
(708)653-4159 fax
Susan Grupp, Horticulture

Edgar County Unit
210 W. Washington
Paris 61944
(217)465-8585
(217)463-1192 fax

Edwards/Wabash Unit
350 N. Seventh
Albion 62806
(618)445-2934
(618)445-3746 fax

Mt. Carmel Office (Wabash County)
RR 1, Box 107
Mt. Carmel 62863
(618)262-5725
(618)263-3370 fax

Effingham/Fayette/Clay Unit
1209 Wenthe Dr.
Effingham 62401
(217)347-7773
(217)347-5150 fax

Louisville Office (Clay County)
235 Chestnut St.
Louisville 62858
(618)665-3328
(618)665-4985 fax

Vandalia Office (Fayette County)
118 N. 6th
Vandalia 62471
(618)283-2753
(618)283-4932 fax

University of Illinois, Cooperative Extension Service—Unit Offices (cont.)

Fayette County

See Effingham/Fayette/Clay

Ford/Iroquois Unit

912 W. Seminary Ave.
P.O. Box 163
Onarga 60955-0163
(815)268-4051
(815)268-4058 fax

Franklin County Unit

RR 3, P.O. Box 364
Benton 62812
(618)439-3178
(618)439-2953 fax

Fulton County Unit

RR 2, Box 37A7
Lewistown 61542
(309)547-3711
(309)547-3713 fax
Matthew P. Montgomery, Crops and Horticulture

Gallatin/Pope-Hardin/Saline Unit

1220 E. Sloan, Suite 1
Harrisburg 62946
(618)252-8391
(618)253-3006 fax

Golconda Office (Pope County)
Corner of Claire and Lewis
Housing Apt. 1 (for UPS mailing)
P.O. Box 97
Golconda 62938
(618)683-8555
(618)683-2704 fax (call first)

Elizabethtown Office (Hardin County)
Apt. 13, Walnut St.
P.O. Box 62
Elizabethtown 62931

Greene/Macoupin Unit

RR 3, Box 129C
Carrollton 62016
(217)942-6996
(217)942-6996 fax

Carlinville Office (Macoupin County)
210 N. Broad St.
Carlinville 62626
(217)854-9604
(217)854-7804 fax

Grundy County Unit

1802 N. Division St., Suite 604
P.O. Box 432
Morris 60450
(815)942-0177
(815)942-2725
(815)942-9519 fax

Hamilton/Wayne/White Unit

Fairfield Office (Wayne County)
#2B Frontier Dr.
Fairfield 62837
(618)842-3702
(618)842-4725 fax

McLeansboro Office (Hamilton County)
Courthouse Basement
McLeansboro 62859
(618)643-3716

Robinson Office (White County)
304 E. Robinson
Carmi 62821
(618)382-2662

Hancock County Unit

550 N. Madison
RR 3, Box 114A
Carthage 62321
(217)357-2150
(217)357-3598 fax

Hardin County

See Gallatin/Pope-Hardin/Saline

Henderson/Mercer/Warren Unit

P.O. Box 227
Monmouth 61462-0227
(309)734-5161
(309)734-5532 fax

Stronghurst Office (Henderson County)
410 E. Main, P.O. Box 540
Stronghurst 61480
(309)924-1163
(309)924-1164 fax

University of Illinois, Cooperative Extension Service—Unit Offices (cont.)

Aledo Office (Mercer County)
702 S.E. Third St.
Aledo 61231
(309)582-5106
(309)582-7338 fax

Henry/Stark Unit

Blackhawk East College, Bldg. 4 (for UPS mailing)
Illinois Rts. 78 and 34
P.O. Box 74
Galva 61434
(309)853-1533
(309)853-1634 fax

Iroquois County
See Ford/Iroquois

Jackson County Unit

R.R. 3, Alva Blacktop (for UPS mailing)
P.O. Box 160
Murphysboro 62966
(618)687-1727
(618)687-1612

Jasper/Cumberland Unit

1401 Clayton
P.O. Box 31
Newton 62448
(618)783-2521
(618)783-2232 fax

Toledo Office (Cumberland County)
Rt. 121 E., P.O. Box 218
Toledo 62468
(217)849-3931
(217)849-2411 fax

Jefferson County Unit

4620 Broadway
Mt. Vernon 62864-9513
(618)242-0780
(618)242-0781 fax

Jersey County
See Calhoun/Jersey

JoDaviess/Carroll Unit

8070 S. Clay St.
Mt. Carroll 61053
(815)244-9444
(815)244-3836 fax

JoDaviess Office
204 Vine
P.O. Box 600
Elizabeth 61028
(815)858-2273
(815)858-2274 fax

Johnson County
See Alexander/Johnson/Massac/
Pulaski/Union

Kane County Unit

535 S. Randall Rd.
St. Charles 60174-1591
(708)584-6166
(708)584-4610 fax

Kankakee County Unit

189 E. Court, Suite 300
Kankakee 60901
(815)939-8120
(815)939-8026 fax

Kendall County Unit

7775B Illinois Rt. 47
Yorkville 60560-9619
(708)553-5824
(708)553-5871 fax
Gary Bretthauer, Crops/IPM

Knox County Unit

180 S. Soangetaha Rd., Suite 108
Galesburg 61401
(309)342-5108
(309)342-1768 fax
Kylen Cecil, Agricultural and Natural Resources
Management

Lake County Unit

100 S. U.S. Highway 45
Grayslake 60030
(708)223-8627
(708)223-9288 fax
Sharon Yiesla, Horticulture

LaSalle County Unit

3101 N. Illinois Rt. 23
Ottawa 61350
(815)433-0707
(815)433-5454 fax

University of Illinois, Cooperative Extension Service—Unit Offices (cont.)

Lawrence County Unit

1406 Locust St.
Lawrenceville 62439
(618)943-5018
(618)943-4968 fax

Lee County Unit

280 W. Wasson Rd.
Amboy 61310
(815)857-3525
(815)857-3527 fax

Livingston County Unit

1412 S. Locust
Pontiac 61764
(815)842-1776
(815)842-6547 fax
Marion Shier, Crops Systems

Logan County Unit

122 S. McLean (for UPS mailing)
P.O. Box 38
Lincoln 62656
(217)732-8269
(217)735-5837 fax

Macon County Unit

985 W. Pershing Rd., Suite G4 (for UPS mailing)
P.O. Box 3428
Decatur 62526-3428
(217)877-6042
(217)877-4564 fax

Macoupin County

See Greene/Macoupin

Madison/St. Clair Unit

Madison Office
900 Hillsboro
Box 427
Edwardsville 62025
(618)692-7700
(618)692-7705 fax

St. Clair Office
#1 S. Third St.
P.O. Box 331
Belleville 62222
(618)236-8600
(618)236-8604 fax

Marion County Unit

1404 E. Main, Illinois Rt. 50 East
Salem 62881
(618)548-1446
(618)548-9891 fax

Marshall/Putnam Unit

300 Edward St.
Henry 61537
(309)364-2356
(309)364-2804 fax

Mason County Unit

133 S. High
P.O. Box 170
Havana 62644
(309)543-3308 (also fax)

Massac County

See Alexander/Johnson/Massac/Pulaski/Union

McDonough County Unit

McDonough Office
3022 W. Jackson
Macomb 61455
(309)837-3939
(309)833-3019 fax

McHenry County Unit

789 McHenry Ave.
P.O. Box 1430
Woodstock 60098
(815)338-4747
(815)338-3737
(815)337-4755 fax

McLean County Unit

402 N. Hershey Rd.
Bloomington 61704
(309)663-8306
(309)663-8270 fax

Menard County

See Sangamon/Menard

Mercer County

See Henderson/Mercer/Warren

Monroe County Unit

901 Illinois Ave,, P.O. Box 117
Waterloo 62298
(618)939-3434
(618)939-7708 fax

University of Illinois, Cooperative Extension Service—Unit Offices (cont.)

Montgomery County Unit

138 E. Wood
Hillsboro 62049
(217)532-3941
(217)532-3944 fax

Morgan/Scott Unit

104 N. Westgate Ave.
Jacksonville 62650
(217)243-7424
(217)243-1544

Scott Office
401 N. Walnut
Winchester 62694
(217)742-9572
(217)742-3852 fax
Duane Friend, Natural Resources Management

Moultrie/Douglas Unit

122 S. Walnut St.
Arthur 61911
(217)543-3755
(217)543-3757 fax

Ogle County Unit

421 Pines Rd., Suite 10
Oregon 61061
(815)732-2191
(815)732-4007 fax
Stan Eden, Crops/Environment

Peoria County Unit

1716 N. University St., Suite 1
Peoria 61604-3901
(309)686-6033
(309)686-8735 fax

Perry County Unit

R.R. 1
Pinckneyville 62274
(618)357-2126

Piatt County Unit

427 W. Marion
Monticello 61856
(217)762-2191
(217)762-2703 fax

Pike County Unit

1301 E. Washington
Pittsfield 62363
(217)285-5543
(217)285-5735 fax

Pope County

See Gallatin/Pope-Hardin/Saline

Pulaski County

See Alexander/Johnson/Massac/
Pulaski/Union

Putnam County Unit

See Marshall/Putnam

Randolph County Unit

313 W. Belmont St.
P.O. Box C
Sparta 62286
(618)443-4364
(618)443-1922 fax

Richland County Unit

306 S. Fair
P.O. Box 130
Olney 62450
(618)395-2191
(618)392-4906 fax

Rock Island County Unit

1414 10th St., Suite 1
Silvis 61282
(309)796-0512
(309)796-0673 fax

St. Clair County

See Madison/St. Clair

Saline County

See Gallatin/Pope-Hardin/Saline

Sangamon/Menard Unit

Illinois State Fairgrounds, Bldg. 30 (for UPS mailing)
P.O. Box 8467
Springfield 62791
(217)782-4617
(217)524-6662 fax

Menard Office
420 S. 7th St.
P.O. Box 138
Petersburg 62675
(217)632-7491
(217)632-2425 fax

University of Illinois, Cooperative Extension Service—Unit Offices (cont.)

Schuyler /Cass
710 Maple Ave. (for UPS mailing)
P.O. Box 287
Rushville 62681
(217)322-3381
(217)322-3382 fax (call first)

Cass Office
651 S. Job
Virginia 62691
(217)452-3211
(217)452-7260 fax

Scott County
See Morgan/Scott

Shelby County Unit
1125 W. N. Second St.
Shelbyville 62565
(217)774-9546
(217)774-9549 fax

St. Clair County
See Madison/St. Clair

Stark County
See Henry/Stark

Stephenson County Unit
University of Illinois, CES
Highland Community College
2998 W. Pearl City Rd., Bldg. R
Freeport 61032
(815)235-4125
(815)232-9006 fax
Robert Lahne, Crops/Animal Systems

Tazewell County Unit
1505 Valle Vista
Pekin 61554-6245
(309)347-6614
(309)347-5472 fax

Union County
See Alexander/Johnson/Massac/
Pulaski/Union

Vermilion County Unit
427 N. Vermilion
Danville 61832
(217)442-8615
(217)442-8628 fax

Wabash County
See Edwards/Wabash

Warren County
See Henderson/Mercer/Warren

Washington County Unit
238 E. St. Louis, P.O. Box 192
Nashville 62263
(618)327-8881
(618)327-8882 fax (call first)

Wayne County
See Hamilton/Wayne/White

White County
See Hamilton/Wayne/White

Whiteside County Unit
100 E. Knox
Morrison 61270
(815)772-4075
(815)772-4077 fax
Gregory Clark, Crops/Natural Resources

Will County Unit
100 Manhattan Rd.
Joliet 60433
(815)727-9296
(815)727-5570 fax

Williamson County Unit
1306 N. Atchison, Suite A
Marion 62959
(618)993-3304

Winnebago County Unit
4311 W. State St.
Rockford 61102
(815)987-7379
(815)987-7881 fax
Barbara A. Larson, Horticulture

Woodford County Unit
117 W. Center (for UPS mailing)
P.O. Box 162
Eureka 61530
(309)467-3789
(309)467-6034 fax
Peter Farndel, Crops